# THE OFFICIAL LIVERPOOL FC QUIZ BOOK

**Published by twocan**

©2019. Published by twocan under licence from Liverpool FC.

**ISBN: 978-1-913362-14-0**

**PICTURE CREDITS:** Action Images, Getty Images.

## COMPILED BY DAVE BALL & GED REA

# INTRODUCTION

**In compiling this quiz book, given the extensive history of this great club, it quickly became evident that it was going to be more difficult knowing what to exclude, rather than what to include. How can we condense the achievements of English football's most successful team into a solitary edition. As it is, we are sure that there will be more than enough to keep even the most knowledgable of 'anoraks' happy.**

This compilation applauds the achievements of many great Liverpool players and managers, since the first Championship was secured in 1900/01. The 100 quizzes include some easier questions, some that will stretch your gray matter a little and some that will test even the most ardent of Reds fans. On the left-hand pages you will find questions on players and managers, both past and present, who have brought pleasure to the Anfield faithful, while the right-hand page quizzes are based on topics synonymous with those chosen personalities.

Hopefully, the questions will bring some fond memories and emotions flooding back, and prompt discussions and debate as to who was the best-ever Liverpool legend or manager, what was the Reds' best campaign or who would make your all-time Liverpool eleven.

As the club's statisticians, we have relied on our own research and that of Eric Doig and the LFChistory.net website.

Good luck with the quizzes. We hope you enjoy them and find them suitably entertaining.

**Dave Ball and Ged Rea**

# JAMES MILNER

1. For which club did Milner make his first-team debut, aged 16 years 309 days back in 2002?

2. Which manager gave James his Liverpool debut?

3. What number shirt has Milly worn in his time at the club?

4. Against which club did he score his 50th career Premier League goal and 14th for Liverpool in a 1-1 draw in 2018?

5. The midfielder played for Manchester City against Liverpool in the League Cup semi-final In 2012, but which former City player scored for Liverpool in the 2-2 draw in the second leg?

6. In 2018/19, Milner was sent-off by his former schoolteacher when playing against which club?

7. In 2010, he played in a League Cup final, being one of five future and former Reds players, and scored a fifth-minute penalty, for which club?

8. Milly's first successful penalty for Liverpool saw him beat Cedric Carrasso when playing against which club in Europe?

9. Who was the goalkeeper in the Swansea side when James scored penalties in 2015 and 2016?

10. In April 2018, he equalled the Champions League assist record (eight) when he helped which player score Liverpool's second goal against Manchester City?

# THE 2018/19 SEASON

11.     Who scored Liverpool's first goal of the league season?

12.     Against which club did Fabinho make his club debut as a late substitute?

13.     Which player left Anfield and joined Fulham on a free transfer?

14.     Which ex-Red played against Liverpool in the last league game of the season, his club's only ever-present during the campaign?

15.     Which club did three players make their Liverpool debuts against in a FA Cup tie?

16.     Trent Alexander-Arnold scored his first away Premier League goal with a 25-yard free kick against which club?

17.     Who scored the club's first goal in the Champions League?

18.     Which player scored against Liverpool in two different competitions?

19.     Only one player scored against the Reds in their first seven league games at Anfield - who was he?

20.     Against which club did Liverpool record 36 shots on goal in a league game in December 2018?

# JORDAN HENDERSON

21. From which club did Liverpool sign Jordan in the summer of 2011?

22. Which manager gave him his debut?

23. Jordan replaced which player as Liverpool captain?

24. In April 2013, the midfielder scored twice in a Reds' shirt for the first time. Who were the opponents on that Saturday evening?

25. Which manager spurned the opportunity to sign the future England captain stating in his autobiography that Jordan's running style put him off?

26. In 2014, Henderson became the first Liverpool player to be sent-off since Jonjo Shelvey was red-carded two years previously. Which player was the victim of his late challenge in added time?

27. In April 2015, Jordan converted a penalty in a 4-1 defeat at which Premier League ground?

28. Jordan has played for three league clubs, doing so with which one while out on loan in 2008/09?

29. For scoring in his club's 2-1 defeat of which side did he win the Carling Goal of the Month in September 2016?

30. Against which club did he play his 300th game for Liverpool in a 2-0 away win in December 2018?

# CAPTAINS

31. Only two players in the Premier League era has captained Liverpool on more occasions than Jordan Henderson, Steven Gerrard and who else?

32. Liverpool's victory in the 1995 Football League Cup saw which man lead his side to Wembley success for the only time?

33. One of Liverpool's most inspiring captains, he led England for the first time in May 1974. Who was he?

34. Kenny Dalglish was the player-manager in 1986, but who lifted the FA Cup at Wembley?

35. Which England International captained Liverpool on his club debut in 1997?

36. Who captained the side in the 1959/60 season, and later trained the team which won the European Cup in 1977?

37. Who led England to FA Youth team glory in the Little World Cup in 1963 and later captained Liverpool?

38. Who captained the Reds in his final appearance for the club in May 2007 against Charlton Athletic?

39. Who captained Liverpool on just one occasion - in March 2016 at Southampton?

40. In which season did the Reds have a record ten different captains?

# ALISSON

41. From which club did Liverpool sign the Brazilian goalkeeper in July 2018?

42. How many goals did Liverpool put past him before his transfer to Anfield?

43. Against which club did he concede a goal for the first time in his Reds career, gifting the goal in his fourth game of the season?

44. How many clean sheets did the Brazilian keep in his debut season in the Premier League?

45. Against which club did the keeper pull off a 91st-minute save in Europe which led Jurgen Klopp to remark "If I knew he was this good, I would have paid double?"

46. Alisson was an understudy at his Italian club to which former Premier League goalkeeper?

47. After winning the Champions League, Alisson won the Copa America beating which country 3-1 in the final?

48. What numbered shirt did he wear in his debut season in 2018/19?

49. How many games did he play in as the Reds won their sixth Champions League?

50. Which was the only club to score three times against the Reds in the league in 2018/19?

51. Who kept goal for Liverpool in the game prior to Alisson's debut?

52. Prior to 2019, who was the last Liverpool goalkeeper to play in a Champions League-winning final?

53. Who won his only England cap against Greece in 2006, an appearance which saw his father pocket nearly £10,000 as the result of a bet made years before, that his son would play for his country before the age of 30?

54. Who was in the Liverpool goal when the Reds won the League Cup in a penalty shoot-out against Cardiff City?

55. When David James was sent-off in May 1993, whose first touch of the ball saw him pick David Phillips' penalty out of the net?

56. In the Sixties, John Ogston made just one appearance as he was understudy to which goalkeeper for three years?

57. Following an 89th-minute injury against Leeds in 1994, who replaced Bruce Grobbelaar to make the first of 213 consecutive appearances?

58. When Paul Harrison moved to Leeds on loan in January 2005, which keeper moved in the opposite direction the same day?

59. Which goalkeeper made the first of only five appearances at Anfield in five years in the 4-2 loss at Derby County in March 1978?

60. In 1908, who became the club's oldest player when playing against Newcastle aged 41 years 165 days?

## QUIZ 7

# SADIO MANE

61. In which year did Sadio join Liverpool?

62. How many goals did he score in the Premier League in 2018/19 to become the joint recipient of the Golden Boot?

63. Against which club did Mane make a goalscoring debut for the Reds?

64. Sadio's 95th-minute winner against Everton in December 2016 came after whose shot had struck the post leaving the striker the opportunity to score?

65. Against which club did the Senegalese score his first Liverpool hat-trick?

66. Sadio's first penalty for the Reds saw him fail to score against which club?

67. In February 2019, Mane showed a moment of true inspiration as his impudent back-heel doubled Liverpool's lead against which club?

68. Whose header gave him the chance to equalise in the 2018 Champions League final?

69. Against which club in March 2019 did Mane become only the fifth player to score in six successive Premier League games at Anfield, which included his 50th goal for the club?

70. Which goalkeeper was beaten on both occasions when Liverpool beat Everton in both games of 2016/17?

71. Which player scored one of his three league goals for Liverpool in the 1-1 draw at Goodison in October 2015?

72. Who was the last player to score a hat-trick in the derby, prior to the 2019/20 season?

73. Which player scored twice in Liverpool's 4-0 defeat of Everton in 2014 prior to missing a penalty which prevented his hat-trick?

74. Who was the first Liverpool goalkeeper to be sent-off in a Merseyside derby?

75. Who in the Seventies scored for both sides in derby fixtures?

76. Which player scored 25 goals for Liverpool in the fixture which included 13 in the league?

77. In 1988, Liverpool won an FA Cup fifth-round tie as a result of whose headed goal?

78. Who converted a penalty kick in the 1977 FA Cup semi-final replay at Maine Road?

79. At Goodison Park in December 1991, which Liverpool player scored the only goal of his Reds career?

80. In 2001/02, which man became the first player to appear for both teams in a derby in the same season?

# DIVOCK ORIGI

81. Which player did Divock replace when he became a Champions League hero in Madrid in 2019?

82. Whose parried shot by Marc-Andre Ter Stegen led to the striker's opening goal against Barcelona in 2019?

83. Which club did Origi play for in the Bundesliga?

84. From whose cross did Origi score a late winner at Newcastle in May 2019?

85. He came on in Europe for his first appearance in over two years in November 2018, playing the final eleven minutes in a 2-0 defeat against which side?

86. Whose mishit shot span high into the air to deceive Jordan Pickford and give Origi his last-minute winner in 2018/19?

87. The Belgian's first goals for the club saw him score a hat-trick at which ground?

88. After signing for the Reds, Origi was then loaned out to which club for the 2014/15 season?

89. Although Divock plays his international football for Belgium, which country did his father Michael represent?

90. Which Evertonian was red carded after his challenge on Origi in April 2016?

# CHAMPIONS LEAGUE 2018/19

91. Who was adjudged to have handled the ball in the final which led to the opening goal?

92. Which former Red scored against Liverpool in the season's campaign?

93. Which club defeated Liverpool by scoring the only goal of a game in the 90th minute?

94. Gini Wijnaldum came on as a substitute to replace which player at half-time to score twice against Barcelona at Anfield?

95. Who was the only player to score an own goal in one of the 13 games in the competition?

96. Which player received a Champions League winners medal for the second time with a different English club, although he did not play in either final?

97. Which team did Liverpool eliminate in the competition for a second successive season?

98. After playing in a 4-0 defeat with Real Madrid in 2009, which outfield player, ten years later was in a side which conceded four again to Liverpool?

99. Which player appeared against Liverpool in both of the Reds last two Champions League winning seasons, 14 years apart?

100. Which player's only appearance in the campaign came as a substitute in the defeat of Red Star?

# FERNANDO TORRES

101. From which club did Liverpool sign the Spaniard in 2007?

102. Against which club did Fernando score his first goal?

103. Who managed Torres at his two English clubs?

104. Torres finished his first season in the Premier League with 24 goals, the first Liverpool player to record 20 or more since which striker?

105. In successive weeks in 2008, Fernando scored two hat-tricks, against Middlesbrough and who else?

106. After scoring winning goals in European Championships at U16 and U19 level, Fernando in 2008 scored the winning goal at senior level, doing so against which country?

107. In the Goodison derby in September 2008, Torres scored the only two goals in the game. Who kept goal for the Blues that day?

108. Against which club did he open the scoring in a 4-0 Anfield Champions League Round of 16, second leg in March 2009?

109. Whose record for most goals scored by an overseas player in his debut Premier League season, did Torres break?

110. After a run of one league win in six games in 2010/11, Torres scored the final goals of his Liverpool career with two in a 3-0 victory at which ground?

# LIVERPOOL V CHELSEA

111.  In April 2014, Willian replaced which player on the hour mark before scoring his club's second goal at Anfield?

112.  Who in October 2000 became the first goalkeeper to score an own-goal in the fixture?

113.  Which player appeared in 47 games against the Reds in his career, 39 of which were with Chelsea and the remainder with West Ham United?

114.  Who in October 1997 became only the fourth player and the first in 67 years to score a hat-trick for Liverpool against the Londoners?

115.  Which player scored the winning goal in the 2007 Champions League semi-final first leg at Stamford Bridge prior to his move to Anfield?

116.  Which player scored three times for Chelsea at Stamford Bridge against the Reds and in May 1991, scored for Liverpool in a 4-2 defeat at the same venue?

117.  Which player scored an unfortunate own-goal at Anfield in the 90th minute to give the visitors a 1-1 draw in the Champions League semi-final first leg?

118.  Which Reds player has made more appearances for Liverpool against Chelsea than any other man?

119.  Three days after losing to them in the 2012 FA Cup final, the Reds beat Chelsea in a league fixture at Anfield. Who scored his first Liverpool league goal that evening?

120.  Which Chelsea player missed a penalty in 1992 and was sent off along with Marcel Desailly at Anfield seven years later?

# DANIEL AGGER

121. After just 49 appearances, Agger moved from which club to join the Reds?

122. His first goal for Liverpool came in the fourth game of the 2006/07 season, against which team?

123. In 2006, the Dane helped Liverpool win the Community Shield by defeating which club?

124. His 2010/11 season ended in April when he sustained an injury while playing against which club?

125. In the 2012 League Cup final, Agger was injured and was replaced near the end of normal time by which player?

126. In Brendan Rodgers' first league game in charge in August 2012, the defender was sent-off against West Brom for fouling which player?

127. In his last game for the Reds, he scored the club's 100th league goal of the season, against which club in May 2014?

128. Agger made his 100th appearance for Liverpool in a 3-1 European victory at Unirea Urziceni. Which country were they from?

129. Against which club did he score his only European away goal, in a 2-1 defeat in April 2010?

130. His only FA Cup goal helped Liverpool towards Wembley when he opened the scoring in the fourth-round defeat of which Premier League club in 2012?

# CENTRAL DEFENDERS

131. Whose book was entitled 'Stand Up Pinocchio'?

132. Who led Liverpool out as captain of the club in the UEFA Cup final against Alaves?

133. In September 2014, Liverpool sent Sebastian Coates out on a season-long loan to which fellow Premier League club?

134. Which player scored in Watford's 3-0 defeat of the Reds and then a last-minute winner for Bournemouth a year later?

135. Not generally renowned as a goalscorer, he did score Liverpool's goal in the 1-0 European Cup win in Athens in the 1985 semi-final, who was he?

136. Which defender failed to score in over 200 games and starred in the 2001 treble-winning side?

137. Which club did Emlyn Hughes manage after his playing career ended?

138. After winning the League and UEFA Cup in 1973, which defender won the European Cup with Nottingham Forest?

139. Whose only goal for the Reds came at a former club, Coventry City, in a 1-0 win in September 1996?

140. Which player was sent-off in both league games against the Reds in 2008/09, the latter game saw Liverpool win 4-1?

# TRENT ALEXANDER-ARNOLD

141. Against which side did Trent score his only goal of the 2018/19 season?

142. What number shirt does he wear?

143. The two full-backs Trent acknowledges he admired most, both played for which country?

144. Did the youngster have more assists in all competitions in 2018/19 than any other Red?

145. Against which club did he record three assists in a Premier League game at Anfield in February 2019?

146. In the game against Southampton in April 2019, who scored his first Liverpool goal from a Trent cross?

147. His debut for the club came in the 2-1 defeat of which club in a League Cup tie at Anfield in October 2016?

148. Of all the places to make a full league debut, Trent earned rave reviews after starring in a 1-1 draw at which ground?

149. With a powerful free-kick, the young full-back scored his first Liverpool goal at the Rhein-Neckar Arena, the home of which club?

150. Trent played in the Euro Nations League third place play-off in 2019 against which country?

# LIVERPOOL YOUNGSTERS

151. Trent Alexander-Arnold broke the record of which 1970s star as the youngest player to appear in a major European club final for the Reds?

152. Aged 16 years and 354 days, who in 2019 became the youngest-ever Red to appear in the FA Cup?

153. Michael Owen in May 1997 became the youngest player to score in league football for Liverpool when he netted against which club?

154. Who against Leeds United became the club's youngest scorer in a League Cup tie, aged 17 years 45 days?

155. David Thompson made his Liverpool debut as an 18-year-old and went on to make 56 appearances, before joining which club in 2000?

156. Which current Liverpool player in 2019 became the Premier League's youngest-ever player, in a game against Wolves?

157. Playing with Rangers in 2019/20, who four years previously became the club's youngest FA Cup scorer in the defeat of Exeter City?

158. Who is the Liverpudlian midfielder who made his debut in the FA Cup in 2019, aged 17?

159. Who is the 17-year-old defender bought in the 2019 close-season from PEC Zwolle?

160. Which 18-year-old was Liverpool's substitute goalkeeper in the 1985 European Cup final?

# XABI ALONSO

161. Xabi played for three clubs which have won the Champions League - Liverpool, Real Madrid and who else?

162. On New Year's Day 2005, the Spaniard broke his ankle playing against which team?

163. Xabi only scored two European goals while at Anfield. Against which opponent did he do it for the first time?

164. In which city did Xabi Alonso win the World Cup?

165. He scored from his own half against Newcastle in 2006, leaving which goalkeeper stranded?

166. His last goal against Charlton in 2007 saw which of his teammates finish his career after 369 games for the Reds?

167. A foul on which Chelsea player in 2005 saw Alonso yellow-carded, which meant he missed the second leg of the Champions League semi-final?

168. He managed 67 minutes of the 2006 FA Cup final before being replaced by which defender?

169. Alonso's second and final goal in Europe for the Reds was a penalty against which team?

170. In the 2010 World Cup final, which player was only yellow-carded despite aiming a Kung Fu style kick at Alonso?

# EUROPEAN CUP CHAMPIONS LEAGUE

171. Which club did the Reds play at Saint-Jakob Stadium in 2002 and again in 2014?

172. Who kept goal for AC Milan in the 2005 and 2007 Finals?

173. Who scored AC Milan's third goal in the Champions League final in 2005?

174. In 1980, Liverpool stayed in the British Isles to play a European Cup tie. Which team did they face?

175. Which Real Madrid player scored for his club in both games against the Reds, in 2014 and the 2018 final?

176. Which Yugoslav side beat Liverpool in 1973 in what was Bill Shankly's last season amongst Europe's elite?

177. Michael Owen scored hat-tricks against Spartak Moscow and which other side?

178. Which Arsenal striker scored in both legs of the Champions League quarter-final in 2007/08?

179. Who was the defender who got married the day before the Inter Milan game at Anfield in 1965?

180. Which player scored once for Sevilla in the 2-2 draw and twice in the 3-3 stalemate against the Reds in 2017?

# JOHN BARNES

181. With which club did he play in his first FA Cup final?

182. On the day he made his Liverpool debut, which other player made his first appearance for the Reds?

183. One of his greatest performances came in the 4-0 defeat of Queens Park Rangers at Anfield when which goalkeeper conceded two goals to the striker?

184. Who was in goal when Barnes scored a hat-trick on the last day of the season in 1990 at Highfield Road?

185. After an injury suffered in August 1991, he returned to the team and scored an FA Cup hat-trick against which club?

186. Against which country did he come on as a substitute in 1986 and create Gary Lineker's consolation goal?

187. Who managed the player at both club and country level?

188. In his last game for Liverpool, which team held the Reds to a 1-1 draw on the last day of the season to end their chance of a Champions League place?

189. He made his Charlton debut as a substitute in 1999 in the 1-0 victory over which side?

190. Barnes' last goal in Europe for the Reds came in a 6-3 defeat of which side in 1996?

191. When Liverpool beat Everton 2-1 in the January 2018 tie, who scored the opening goal?

192. Prior to 2019/20, who was the last player to score against the Reds in the competition before moving to Anfield?

193. Who was the last Liverpool player to score in both the FA Cup semi-final and final in the same season?

194. Which was the only side to win an FA Cup game at Anfield between 1970 and 1990?

195. After winning the 2006 final in exciting style, Liverpool's hold on the Cup was released in Round Three the following year, by which club?

196. Which club have Liverpool beaten in four FA Cup semi-finals since the war, yet went on to lose all those subsequent finals?

197. In a break with tradition, the Third Round in 1999/2000 took place before Christmas. Who did Liverpool defeat 2-0?

198. In 2001, Liverpool's FA Cup semi-final opponents were in the semi-final for the only time in their history. Who were they?

199. From whose cross did Ian St John head home the goal which finally brought the FA Cup to Anfield in 1965?

200. In the 1971 FA Cup final, Peter Thompson became the first Liverpool substitute to come on at Wembley in the competition, when he replaced which player?

201. Benitez's first venture into the FA Cup saw the Reds lose 1-0 away to which team?

202. Rafa's first ever European game in charge of the Reds in 2004 was a 2-0 win in Austria. Who scored both of the goals?

203. Who, by joining the club in 2007, became Rafa's costliest signing?

204. Against which club did Liverpool play their earliest game of a new season - July 13th 2005?

205. Which player was brought off the bench in 2007/08 and scored seven times?

206. In 2006, Benitez suffered European elimination for the first time, losing to which club 3-0 on aggregate?

207. Who was the only Liverpool player to miss a penalty in the FA Cup final shoot-out with West Ham United in 2006?

208. Which club did Liverpool meet in Rafa's first final appearance?

209. Against which club did the manager see Liverpool draw 1-1 in a European qualifier in the Ukraine in August 2006?

210. Whose 44th and final Liverpool appearance in Europe came in the 2007 Champions League semi-final at Anfield against Chelsea?

# THE RAFA YEARS

211. Who in 2009, became the first Liverpool player to score a winning goal at the Bernabeu?

212. Which goalkeeper's last appearance for the Reds came in the 5-3 defeat of Luton in 2006?

213. Who scored his only goal for Liverpool in the 2005 League Cup final?

214. In the Anfield derby in March 2006, Harry Kewell was among the Liverpool scorers. Which fellow countryman netted for the Blues?

215. Who scored for Reading in their FA Cup elimination of Liverpool in 2010 and later for Everton in the competition eight years later?

216. Which Newcastle United player was sent-off at Anfield during the 2005/06 season for the second successive time at the ground?

217. Which club did the Reds play at the Arnold Schwarzenegger Stadium?

218. For which team did Richard Pacquette score against Liverpool in January 2008?

219. Who played for Chelsea against the Reds in the Champions League in the 2005/06 season, having scored against Liverpool in the previous season's campaign?

220. Who scored Juventus' only goal in the two games against the Reds in the Champions League in 2004/05?

# EMRE CAN

221. From which club did Liverpool sign the player in July 2014?

222. Emre has now played for three clubs which have won the Champions League - Liverpool, Juventus and which other club?

223. Can scored the first goal of Jurgen Klopp's reign at Anfield, but in which competition?

224. Voted the club's Goal of the Season in 2016/17, the German scored with an acrobatic overhead kick against which club?

225. Against which team did he make his last appearance in a Reds shirt?

226. Can was sent-off for the only time while at Anfield, seeing red in a 4-1 loss to which club?

227. In a Champions League game in August 2017, Can scored twice in the opening 21 minutes. Who were Liverpool playing?

228. In Liverpool's run to the 2018 Champions League final, he found the net once in the group stage, against which team?

229. In February 2016, he was one of six different scorers in the defeat of which club?

230. Can made his Liverpool debut in a defeat at Manchester City. Which £20 million teammate also made his first appearance in that match?

# THE GERMAN CONNECTION

231. Didi Hamann played against Liverpool in 1998 for Newcastle and ten years later for which club against the Reds?

232. Which German scored his only European goal for the Reds in a final?

233. Karlheinz Riedle upon leaving Anfield played for, and was then caretaker manager with Roy Evans, of which club?

234. Which ground staged Liverpool's first European final?

235. Which player joined Liverpool in August 2000 after twice winning the Bundesliga with Bayern Munich and also with AC Milan in Serie A?

236. Which German side met Liverpool twice in pre-season friendlies (2006 and 2016) winning both games, 5-0 and 4-0?

237. Who played for Bayer Leverkusen in two Champions League fixtures in 2005 and later played 40 times for Liverpool?

238. How was the European tie with Cologne in 1965 resolved?

239. Who against Bayern Munich in March 1971 scored the first hat-trick in a European game?

240. Who scored for Borussia Dortmund in the 2016 Europa League and then played for Bayern Munich in two games against the Reds in the Champions League three years later?

# JAMIE CARRAGHER

241. Jamie's first goal came on his full debut when he headed home against which team at Anfield?

242. Of all the teams to score two own goals against in the same game, which club profited from them in September 1999?

243. Against which country did he miss a retaken penalty in a 2006 World Cup shoot-out?

244. How many times did the defender win the League Cup?

245. Which manager gave the young Carragher his first-team debut?

246. Against which club did Jamie break his leg in September 2003, an injury which sidelined him for four months?

247. 'Carra' moved from right-back to left-back when which player took his position in the Liverpool team?

248. Captaining the side on his last appearance for the Reds, he hit the woodwork while playing against which opponents?

249. Jamie finished with 737 appearances for his club, with only one player having surpassed his total. Who is he?

250. Against which team was he sent-off in an FA Cup game?

# 2005 CHAMPIONS LEAGUE

251. Three Liverpool players started all 15 of Liverpool's European Cup games in 2004/05. Jamie Carragher and Sami Hyypia were two. Name the other?

252. Steven Gerrard captained Liverpool in the Istanbul final. Who skippered the Reds' opponents?

253. Which Liverpool player was fouled in the box by Gennaro Gattuso that led to the award of a penalty in the second half of the final?

254. Three months after breaking his ankle in a league game, who returned to the team for the away leg against Juventus in Turin?

255. Who sat on the bench for Liverpool's first game of the campaign and never appeared for the club again?

256. Name the only Italian to take a penalty for AC Milan in the shoot-out in Istanbul?

257. Which Liverpool player committed the foul that led to AC Milan's first-minute opener in the final?

258. Who was the referee that ruled that Luis Garcia's shot had crossed the line in the semi-final against Chelsea at Anfield?

259. Who made six appearances for the Reds in Europe that season, including one in the final, all as a substitute?

260. Luis Garcia scored to give Liverpool a two-goal lead over Juventus in the quarter-final at Anfield. Who making his first start for over a year, supplied him with the pass?

# PHILIPPE COUTINHO

261. From which club did the Reds sign the Brazilian for just £8.5 million in 2013?

262. At which lower league team did he score a 91st-minute winner in a FA Cup fourth-round replay?

263. Prior to his move to Barcelona, Coutinho had played in Spain while on loan playing for which club?

264. In the penultimate match of his debut season at Anfield, his pass allowed which player to complete a hat-trick at Fulham?

265. Against which club did the Brazilian scored the only goal of the opening game of the 2015/16 season?

266. After scoring in the 2016 League Cup final, which goalkeeper thwarted him in the shoot-out?

267. Which goalkeeper was beaten twice by Coutinho on the opening day of the 2016/17 season, one a 30-yard free-kick?

268. Philippe captained Liverpool for the first time in a European game at Anfield in December 2017. Who were the opposition?

269. He scored in three successive league games in December 2017, failing to do so in the fourth, his last appearances in a Reds shirt. Who was this against?

270. He scored three times for Barcelona in the 2018/19 Champions League campaign. Against which team did the third goal come?

# TRANSFER MARKET

271. In the same month Philippe Coutinho moved to Anfield, which played joined the club from Chelsea?

272. Which club has sold two players to Liverpool for a fee exceeding £30 million?

273. Who was signed by Kenny Dalglish for £350,000 in January 1991 despite being only 17-years-old?

274. Liverpool and Southampton have transfer history. Which player was the first to move to St Mary's from Anfield for a fee of £20million?

275. Which defender came to Liverpool in 1974 from Northampton and won his first medals with the Reds two years later?

276. Oyvind Leonhardsen and John Scales both left Anfield in the Nineties, joining which London club?

277. In 1995, which Irishman made the journey north when he joined Liverpool from Millwall?

278. In 2002, Nicolas Anelka arrived on loan. Which club was the Frenchman playing for at the time?

279. In 1997, who became the first Liverpool player to sign for the club under the Bosman ruling?

280. One of Liverpool's greatest strikers, from which club did Liverpool sign Albert Stubbins in September 1946?

# PETER CROUCH

281. Against which club did Peter score his first-ever hat-trick in club football?

282. Against which Lithuanian club did he make his Liverpool debut in July 2005?

283. After 18 games without a goal, Crouch finally broke his duck when he scored twice against which club?

284. In that game, which member of Liverpool's 2001 treble-winning side was in the opposition defence?

285. In November 2007, the England striker scored the first and eighth goal in a Champions League defeat of which club?

286. Which midfielder gave way to Crouch in the 2007 Champions League final in Athens?

287. For which club did the striker make his last Anfield appearance?

288. For which club did he play 16 times against Liverpool scoring three times?

289. In Liverpool's route to the FA Cup final success in 2006, Crouch scored twice in a 7-0 win at which ground in the Sixth Round?

290. In the last of his five League Cup games for Liverpool, Crouch was sent-off for a two-footed challenge on which Chelsea player in December 2007?

291. Which Liverpool player scored 12 goals in his 17 appearances against the Londoners?

292. Which goalkeeper conceded 17 goals in the last five of his 36 appearances against the Reds 2004-2017?

293. On which ground did Liverpool defeat Arsenal in the second replay of a League Cup tie in November 1988?

294. In the 1998 World Cup, Golden Boot winner David Suker had his penalty saved by which goalkeeper in August 1999 in the 90th minute?

295. Who besides Michael Thomas scored for the Gooners at Anfield in the May 1989 title decider?

296. Which goalkeeper conceded five goals at Anfield in December 2018?

297. From whose pass did Michael Owen run through to score the 2001 FA Cup winner?

298. Who came on in the 78th minute to score Liverpool's fourth and final goal in the 90th minute of the 4-2 Champions League quarter-final win in 2008?

299. Who played in Arsenal's 1971 FA Cup final win and later managed the Londoners against the Reds?

300. When Robbie Fowler had his controversial penalty saved in 1997, who followed up to score his first league goal for the Reds?

301. Against which team did Kenny score his only domestic Cup final goal for the Reds?

302. Who was the most expensive purchase in Kenny's second spell in the manager's seat?

303. On May 1st 1990, Kenny made his final appearance in a Red shirt coming on as a substitute for Jan Molby against which club?

304. Kenny Dalglish's first signing for Liverpool later went on to play for England. Who was he?

305. In 1978, he scored twice for Liverpool in the 7-0 demolition of which team at Anfield?

306. Which team did the Reds defeat 6-1 in an FA Cup tie at Anfield in February 2012 with the help of two own-goals?

307. In January 1984, Kenny suffered a depressed fracture of the cheekbone in a collision with which Manchester United player?

308. Who was the last Liverpool player to score a goal in Kenny Dalglish's first spell as manager?

309. In August 1977, Kenny scored on his league debut at which club?

310. A crowd of over 30,000 saw Dalglish's testimonial in 1990/91. Which former Anfield star played for Real Sociedad that night?

# CUP COMPETITIONS

311. Who kept goal for the club when they contested their first European Cup final?

312. Who in 1996 came on as a substitute in the FA Cup and scored to record his 42nd goal in the tournament?

313. Which lower league team knocked the Reds out of the League Cup in 2010 after a penalty shoot-out?

314. Which former Premier League player scored in both legs of the 2010 Europa League semi-final for Atletico Madrid?

315. Who was the first overseas player to score against the Reds in an FA Cup final?

316. Which Greek side did Liverpool beat in the UEFA Cup in 2001 by an aggregate score of 4-2?

317. Which former Liverpool player was in the Bolton team that faced the Reds in the 1995 League Cup final?

318. Steven Gerrard scored in both legs of the 2005 League Cup semi-final, doing so against which club?

319. With Neville Southall injured, which goalkeeper replaced him in the Merseyside FA Cup final In 1986?

320. Which team were beaten 5-3 on their home ground by Liverpool in the Europa League in 2012?

# FABINHO

321. Fabinho's first three games for Liverpool came in three different competitions. Who were their opponents on his Premier League debut?

322. His League Cup debut saw which player score a late winner at Anfield?

323. For which team did he once play in a Champions League semi-final before he joined the Reds?

324. For which club did the Brazilian make just one appearance in May 2013?

325. Which player's suspension resulted in Fabinho playing out of position in a game with Bayern Munich at Anfield in February 2019?

326. What number shirt did he wear in the 2019 Champions League final?

327. Fabinho's first goal for the Reds came on Boxing Day 2018, his team's fourth, after he had replaced which player?

328. His Liverpool debut came in September 2018, coming on for Sadio Mane in the 3-2 defeat of which club?

329. Against which English club did he score in a 3-1 win in the Champions League in March 2017?

330. Fabinho was booked in both legs of a Champions League game in 2018/19 against which club?

# THE SOUTH AMERICAN CONNECTION

331. Which goalkeeper was dismissed after only 25 minutes at Blackburn in April 2012, which as a result ruled him out of the FA Cup semi-final against Everton?

332. Mark Gonzalez was the first player from which country to play for the Reds?

333. Which future Liverpool player scored an outstanding volleyed winner in extra-time against Mexico in the World Cup of 2006?

334. Which player appeared in two Champions League finals for Valencia before his move to Anfield in 2005?

335. In which country did the Reds play São Paulo in the 2005 World Club Championship final?

336. In the 1981 World Club Championship final, which legendary figure captained Liverpool's victors?

337. Who scored his first goal with a spectacular volley for the Reds in the 3-2 loss at Loftus Road in March 2012?

338. Who was the Peruvian who in 2007 scored the winning goal from the penalty spot for Newcastle against Liverpool, playing in the same side as James Milner?

339. Whose goal in the 1-0 defeat of Plymouth Argyle in 2017 was the last of his seven goals for the Reds?

340. Against which team in December 2017 did Philippe Coutinho score his only Liverpool hat-trick?

341. Roberto Firmino's winner against Paris Saint-Germain in September 2018 came just three days after he suffered an eye injury against which team?

342. In which year did Bobby move to Anfield?

343. For which team did Firmino play against Jurgen Klopp's Borussia Dortmund side?

344. Against which country did Firmino score for Brazil in the semi-final of the 2019 Copa America?

345. The Brazilian netted the club's 1,000th Anfield Premier League goal in a defeat of which club in 2018/19?

346. Against which club Bobby score in both legs of a Champions League tie in 2018/19?

347. Firmino's first league goal for Liverpool came in a win at which team in 2015?

348. At the end of the 2018/19 season, which was Roberto's favourite club, having scored eight times against them?

349. In September 2011, Bobby and which former Red scored for Hoffenheim in a 4-0 defeat of Mainz?

350. Against which club did the striker score and miss a penalty in the 2017/18 season in European competition?

# GOALSCORERS

351. Against which club did Peter Crouch win the vote for the best acrobatic goal scored in the Champions League?

352. Who scored a Champions League hat-trick in 2007 and scored his last goal in Europe in the 2010 Europa League semi-final at Anfield?

353. Which Liverpool player has scored in the most successive seasons for the club?

354. Prior to 2019/20, Liverpool had won four away games in the Premier League by a 6-0 margin. In the second of them, against which side did Michael Owen hit four?

355. When Mo Salah scored four times against Watford in a 5-0 home win in 2018, who scored the Reds other goal?

356. Which player scored Liverpool's last goal in the old First Division?

357. Which former Liverpool player returned to the Premier League in 2018/19 and netted against the Reds?

358. Which forward was substituted by the Reds in both legs of the UEFA Cup final in 1976?

359. Against which club did Kevin Keegan make his last Liverpool appearance on British soil?

360. Who was the first striker to score four times against the Reds in a Premiership game?

# STEVEN GERRARD

361. On which ground did Steven score twice from the penalty spot and miss a third in a Premier League game in March 2014?

362. Against which team did he score his fourth hat-trick for the club, this coming in an Anfield European fixture?

363. The England midfielder's famous FA Cup final against West Ham United saw him score twice in normal time against which goalkeeper?

364. Which manager gave Steven his debut in the game against Blackburn in 1998?

365. In which city did Steven famously score his first England goal?

366. In the 1999 derby in April, Steven twice cleared off the line when which goalkeeper was beaten in the final minutes?

367. In February 2003, Steven Gerrard was banned for three games for a tackle in a Merseyside derby on which player, which had gone unpunished at the time?

368. Steven famously scored in his last game in a Reds shirt, but what was the score in the game?

369. Stevie G scored a hat-trick against an English club for the first time in 2008. Who were the opposition?

370. In November 1998, Steven came on for his debut as a substitute against Blackburn, replacing which player?

# ON THE SPOT

371. Against which club did James Milner score a penalty in both meetings in the Champions League group stages in 2018/19?

372. Kevin Keegan, Phil Neal, Mo Salah and which other player have converted a penalty for the Reds in a European final?

373. Who scored eight penalties for Liverpool in the 1990/91 season?

374. Which Liverpool player converted a 117th-minute penalty equaliser at Tottenham in the League Cup in December 2004 and then scored the decisive spot-kick in the shoot-out?

375. Who was the first goalkeeper to save a Wembley FA Cup final penalty?

376. In 1993, both John Barnes and Mike Marsh missed second half spot-kicks in the Reds 1-0 defeat of which club?

377. Which Southampton player's spot-kick was saved by Simon Mignolet at St Mary's in 2016?

378. In Liverpool's 10-0 defeat of Fulham in 1986, which player scored four times and missed a penalty?

379. With the scores level at 1-1 in the 1979 FA Cup semi-final against Manchester United, which player missed a penalty in a game which ended 2-2?

380. Who scored eight times and missed once from the spot in the 1954/55 season?

# JOE GOMEZ

381. Which manager gave Joe his full international debut?

382. Which number shirt did the defender wear in 2018/19?

383. Against which side did Gomez suffer his leg fracture in December 2018?

384. The young defender in September 2017 became the first Liverpool player sent-off in the Champions League for three years when he was red-carded against which club?

385. For which club did Gomez play, prior to his Anfield move?

386. Joe made his England debut in November 2017 coming on as a substitute for which Manchester United player?

387. The youngster came on in the last minute of the Champions League final when he replaced which player?

388. Joe started his first game in a Reds shirt assisting which player's 86th-minute winning goal in a 1-0 win at Stoke?

389. Gomez made his European debut in a 1-1 draw away to which club in September 2015?

390. In which position did he make his league debut for the Reds?

# LONDON CONNECTION

391. Like Joe Gomez, which future England midfielder came to Anfield from the same club?

392. Which Liverpool player between 2005-2013, played against the Reds for West Ham, Arsenal and Chelsea?

393. Which team did Liverpool defeat 9-0 in September 1989?

394. Who kept goal for West Ham when they were hammered 4-0 at the London Stadium in May 2017 and 4-1 at Anfield the following February?

395. Who played for Crystal Palace, Queens Park Rangers and Millwall before moving to Anfield in 1991, only to be transferred to Arsenal after eight appearances for the Reds?

396. Against which club did Steven Gerrard miss a penalty and then score the winner on 87 minutes towards the end of his final season with Liverpool?

397. Which member of Liverpool's 2001 treble-winning team later played for Charlton, Tottenham and Fulham?

398. Which Champions League winner made the first of his 30 appearances against the Reds in 1988 and last against them in the 2006 FA Cup final?

399. After keeping in two draws against the Reds with Sevilla, who was the Fulham keeper in both defeats by Liverpool the following season?

400. When Liverpool regained their top-flight status in 1962, which club were promoted with them?

# DIETMAR HAMANN

401. For which team did Didi play in his first FA Cup final?

402. In December 1998, he was sent-off playing in an away game prior to his Anfield move. Which team was this against?

403. The German was one of six debutants for the Reds on the opening day of the 1999/2000 season, only for his contribution to be cut short due to injury against which club?

404. Who did he replace in the Istanbul final of 2005 to make such an important impact?

405. In that 2005 European run, he scored his last goal in a Reds shirt, ironically against which German club?

406. Against which club did he play his last game for the club, coming on as a 71st-minute substitute?

407. Didi played in a World Cup final during his time at Anfield, but suffered defeat against which country?

408. What shirt number did he wear throughout his time on Merseyside?

409. In September 2000, he scored twice in a 3-2 defeat of which side at Anfield?

410. Which two of his teammates in the 1996 UEFA Cup final also moved to Anfield?

# LIVERPOOL & NEWCASTLE UNITED

411. Who had a goal disallowed in the 1974 FA Cup final against the 'Toon'?

412. Three managers have been in charge of both Liverpool and Newcastle - Rafa Benitez, Kenny Dalglish and who else?

413. Who was the only Newcastle player to score in both of the 4-3 games at Anfield in the Nineties?

414. Georginio Wijnaldum was the second player to move to Liverpool for a fee of over £20 million, but who was the first?

415. Prior to the start of the 2019/20 season, who was the only Newcastle player to hit a Premier League hat-trick in the fixture, doing so in November 1993?

416. Who in May 2001 was the last Liverpool player to score three goals in a game against the Geordies?

417. Which member of Liverpool's 2012 FA Cup final side was the first to score for seven different sides in the Premier League, a tally which included 27 for Newcastle?

418. Who played for the Geordies in the fixture at St James' Park in October 2017, having previously made 69 appearances for the Reds 2010-13?

419. Who scored four of his five Liverpool goals in January 2004, which included both in the FA Cup win over Newcastle?

420. Who in 1977 was the last Liverpool player to miss a penalty prior to the start of the 2019/20 season?

# GERARD HOULLIER

421. In which stadium did Gerard win his first two trophies as Liverpool boss?

422. Defeat by which club in a League Cup tie in November 1998 ended the joint-managerial partnership of Houllier and Roy Evans?

423. In which city did Liverpool play their first game without Gerard Houllier, who was recovering from heart surgery?

424. Against which club did Houllier's team trail 3-0 at half-time in a Champions League game in 2002, before coming back to draw the match?

425. Which of Houllier's signings made his Liverpool debut in October 2000, aged 35 years 237 days?

426. On December 17th 2000, Gerard celebrated his 100th game in sole charge with Danny Murphy scoring the winner at which ground?

427. In Houllier's memorable 2000/01 season, which team did Liverpool play in the last of their 63 games?

428. Who scored in the 2001 League Cup final and was brought on as substitute in that season's FA Cup final?

429. His first signing was also the first French player to join the club. Who was he?

430. The biggest Premiership win during Houllier's reign was a 7-1 defeat of which club in 1999?

# ALL THINGS FRENCH

431. Which player came to the club on loan in December 2001 and scored his first goal in the FA Cup win over Birmingham the following month?

432. Bruno Cheyrou's brother Benoit played for which club against the Reds in two European campaigns?

433. Two Liverpool-based Norwegians played in the 1998 World Cup in France, Stig Inge Bjornebye and who else?

434. Who was a member of the victorious French squad in that World Cup who played only five games in his time at Anfield?

435. Which French side did the Reds meet in their European Cup campaign in 1977?

436. Prior to 2019/20, who has been the most expensive player to arrive at Anfield from a French club?

437. Which Liverpool player appeared in the most games in Euro 2016, six in total which included the semi-final?

438. Whose last two goals for Liverpool came in April 2016 against Borussia Dortmund and Everton?

439. Who is the only Frenchman to score for the Reds in an FA Cup final?

440. Who in 2018 scored in the World Cup final and then against Liverpool in the Champions League?

441. Who was Liverpool's Chief Scout and former defender who was instrumental in the club signing Sami Hyypia?

442. Sami moved to Holland having spent four years at a club which had been beaten by Liverpool in the European Cup Winners' Cup in 1996. Which club was this?

443. Who was Hyypia's centre-back partner in his first four years at Liverpool?

444. Sami rated the best of his 35 goals for the Reds as coming in the defeat of which club during the 2005 Champions League campaign?

445. Against which club did the Finn receive his only red card in his Anfield career?

446. In May 2009, he made his last appearance in a Red shirt, coming on as a late replacement for Steven Gerrard, but who was this against?

447. After leaving Liverpool, which club did he lead to third place in the Bundesliga in 2012/13?

448. Sami Hyypia scored against two Manchester United goalkeepers during his time at Anfield. Massimo Taibi was one, who was the other?

449. In June 2014, the player was named as manager of which Football League Championship Club?

450. Which Liverpool player was signed on loan by Hyypia during the 2014/15 season?

# THE NORDIC COUNTRIES

451. Which of Sami Hyypia's teammates won the European Cup with Ajax?

452. Who scored against Liverpool for Chelsea in the league, for Barcelona in the Champions League and Bolton in the FA Cup?

453. Which Norwegian defender came on a free transfer to Anfield in January 1997 and made 54 appearances in his two-year spell on Merseyside?

454. Who was the first Liverpool player to play for Denmark in a World Cup finals?

455. Who is the only Swede to win a First Division Championship with the Reds?

456. Who scored for Wimbledon against Liverpool in November 1996 and moved to Anfield the following year, where he would score against Tottenham, his future employers?

457. Which Dane made all of his 21 appearances for Liverpool in 2010/11?

458. Which Danish team did Liverpool defeat in the First Round of their successful 1983/84 European Cup campaign?

459. Who won a European Championship medal in 1992 against Germany in Sweden and came to Anfield shortly afterwards?

460. Who was Liverpool's only World Cup representative in 1994 and went on to play seven times in his two Finals tournaments?

461. When Keegan returned with Newcastle in the FA Cup in 1984, which other former Anfield favourite also played?

462. Against which club did the England international play his last game for the Reds?

463. Kevin scored against which club in both legs of a European final?

464. From whose pass did Keegan score his second goal in the 1974 FA Cup final which left commentator David Coleman to remark "Goals pay the rent and Keegan does his share"?

465. Against which club did he score after only two minutes in a European Cup quarter-final at Anfield in 1977?

466. In January 1974, Keegan scored twice at Anfield in an FA Cup tie, but the Reds were surprisingly held to a 2 -2 draw by his home town club. Which team was it?

467. For which player did Keegan famously set up the winner at the Nou Camp in March 1976?

468. In which year did Kevin and Billy Bremner both receive their marching orders at Wembley?

469. Keegan scored the second goal in a FA Cup semi-final replay in 1974 against which club?

470. For which team did Keegan score his only goal against the Reds in 1982?

# FORMER PLAYERS

471. Which ex-Liverpool defender played with Mike Marsh at Coventry and West Ham?

472. Which former Liverpool forward scored twice against the Reds for Oldham in a League Cup tie in 1985?

473. Which former Liverpool player was appointed as Fulham's Chief Operating Officer in 1997?

474. Who scored Aston Villa's winning goal on the last day of the 2010/11 season against the Reds and immediately joined the Anfield staff?

475. Who left Anfield as a player and later became the first manager to win the European Cup with an English team?

476. Which club did Phil Neal manage between 1993-1995?

477. Which former Reds player sold Virgil van Dijk to Liverpool?

478. For which club did Lucas Leiva play immediately after his ten seasons at Anfield?

479. Prior to the start of the 2019/20 season, Nigel Clough had managed once against Liverpool. Which team was he in charge of?

480. Which winger played under Graeme Souness at Liverpool and Rangers and was known for his stepover?

# NABY KEITA

481. In 2018/19, Naby scored the second quickest goal for Liverpool, in just 15 seconds, but against which club?

482. Against which country was he an unused substitute in a 3-0 defeat at the 2019 Africa Cup of Nations, losing to the eventual winners of the competition?

483. At which club did Keita play briefly with Sadio Mane in 2014?

484. For which international side does Naby play?

485. Injury against which team saw him leave the field early in the game and cause him to miss the Champions League final?

486. The midfielder scored his first Liverpool goal with a deft header in April 2019, against which club?

487. Keita took just five minutes of a Champions League game to register his first European goal for the Merseysiders. Who were the opposition?

488. Liverpool fans got their first sighting of Keita in a Reds shirt during a pre-season friendly in 2018 when they faced which non-League team?

489. He was named in the 'Squad of the Season' for the 2017/18 Europa League season, playing for which team?

490. At Salzburg, which former Liverpool goalkeeper, who never made a senior appearance, was a teammate of Naby's?

# AFRICANS

491. Two of Liverpool's FA Cup winning team of 1986 were born on the continent of Africa. Bruce Grobbelaar and who else?

492. Which goalkeeper made seven appearances for the Reds, all in Cup games in 2007/08, and was in the side beaten by Barnsley?

493. Which player appeared in World Cups for Cameroon and became the first player ever to be sent-off at two Finals tournaments?

494. Which player made a scoring debut for Liverpool against Sheffield Wednesday before his transfer to West Ham in 2000?

495. Who were the brothers that played against each other in the League Cup final of 2016?

496. Which player played for Rafa Benitez at Valencia and was in his side in the 2006 FA Cup final?

497. Who was signed by Liverpool in 2003, stayed at Anfield for three years without making a first-team appearance and went on to win over 50 caps for Algeria?

498. Which country did Oussama Assaidi represent at international level?

499. Which player came to Anfield in 2002 and scored the goal which sent the Reds to the top of the league, beating Leeds United in the October?

500. Which goalkeeper starred in a South African touring side in 1924, joined Liverpool and went on to play 338 games for the club?

# JURGEN KLOPP

501. At which club did Jurgen spend his entire career as a player?

502. Against which club did he remark after a Mo Salah goal in 2019, "It blew me away"... "I was the first person in the stadium to know it was going in"?

503. Liverpool gained Klopp's 100th win as a manager in the 4-0 defeat of which club in 2018/19?

504. Which member of the Borussia Dortmund Champions League final team later joined the Anfield squad?

505. Joining Liverpool in January 2016, who was the first player signed by Jurgen costing over £5 million - from Red Star Belgrade?

506. Name the two players he sold to Bournemouth for fees of over £10million in his first three years in charge?

507. Against which club did Klopp make his bow as manager of the Reds?

508. His first game in Europe saw the club draw 1-1 with Rubin Kazan - who scored the Liverpool goal, the first to do so in the German's tenure?

509. Who scored the first Liverpool goal in a European final in which the manager was Jurgen Klopp?

510. Which was the first side to beat Liverpool in the successful 2018/19 season?

# MANAGERS

511. Pep Guardiola was the first to reach the FA Cup and League Cup in the same season since which manager?

512. The first game in charge of Liverpool for both Graeme Souness and Roy Evans came against the same team. Which one?

513. Who was the first to manage both Liverpool and England?

514. Against which club did Liverpool play their first League Cup final under Kenny Dalglish?

515. Michael Thomas was signed by the same manager when he joined both Liverpool and Benfica. Who was he?

516. Against which club in March 2002 did Gerard Houllier return to the Anfield hot seat after his illness and inspire a Champions League win?

517. Against which club did Liverpool appear in an FA Cup final under Bob Paisley?

518. During the Evans - Houllier managerial partnership which Norwegian was the only player the club signed?

519. Who managed Liverpool to their first League title success after the Second World War?

520. Roy Evans played in just one European game for Liverpool doing so in 1970 against which club?

# DIRK KUYT

521. Dirk in 2011 scored a penalty, and later in the year missed one in league games against which club?

522. In October 2008 Liverpool came from two goals down to win 3-2 with Kuyt netting a last minute winner against which club?

523. When the Dutchman scored the winning penalty in a 2-1 win at Goodison, whose shot had been handled on the line in the last minute?

524. In 2005, Kuyt was the leading scorer in Holland scoring 29 goals for which club?

525. With the Reds waiting seven months for an away league win, Dirk scored past which former Reds keeper In a 4-0 win at Wigan in December 2006?

526. At the start of the 2008/09 season he scored the all important winner in extra time in the Champions League third-round qualifier against which team?

527. After scoring 71 goals in 285 games for the Reds, which club did he sign for in 2012?

528. Which player did Kuyt replace in extra time in the 2012 League Cup final before scoring five minutes later?

529. Dirk is one of only two players from mainland Europe to score ten or more Champions League goals for Liverpool. Who is the other?

530. Against which club did he score three times in a league match in 2011, and the following year net an FA Cup fourth round winner in the 88th minute?

# PENALTIES

531. Who was the last player to score a penalty for Liverpool in the 2018/19 season?

532. Who in October 2018 missed a penalty against the Reds which would have given his side the lead with only minutes to go?

533. Loris Karius saved which England player's penalty during a game in February 2018?

534. At Tottenham in August 2014 Steven Gerrard surpassed which player's record total of 42 successful spot kicks for the club?

535. In Liverpool's 4-3 opening day away win in August 2016 Simon Mignolet denied which Arsenal player on the half hour?

536. In August 2018 at Selhurst Park Mo Salah was fouled by which former Liverpool player to enable James Milner to give the Reds the lead?

537. Having not missed a spot-kick in nearly eight years which Southampton goalkeeper saved a James Milner penalty in May 2017?

538. Tommy Smith and Kevin Keegan both missed spot kicks in the same game in 1973. Who were Liverpool's opponents that day?

539. Who scored 228 goals in 534 appearances for the club which included 34 penalties before finishing his career in 1960?

540. Who scored his first penalty for the club in the 1965 FA Cup semi-final defeat of Chelsea?

# ADAM LALLANA

541. Against which club in January 2016 did Adam score a late winner in a 5-4 win?

542. And in that game who was the defender introduced up front as a nuisance, one of only four games he played for the Reds?

543. Who was his former teammate who played against him in the 2018 Champions League final?

544. Shortly before the midfielder signing for Liverpool which of his Southampton teammates had arrived to make 36 appearances and score three goals?

545. Adam had a short spell on loan in 2007 at a club he had been with as a youngster. Which club was this?

546. Who did Lallana replace in the 2018 Champions League final?

547. Lallana scored eight goals in 2016/17, but against which club did he score twice in an away win and once at Anfield, both games finishing 3-0?

548. In September 2016 he scored a late winner when netting his first England goal in a 1-0 defeat of which country in a World Cup Qualifier?

549. Against which club did he score an 81st-minute goal in a Europa League semi-final?

550. His only FA Cup goal was the winner in a 2-1 defeat of which club in the fifth round In 2015?

# LATE WINNERS

551. Liverpool have beaten Everton five times in the Premier League with goals in the 90th minute or later, but who scored the first of these in 1992/93?

552. Wolves made their first league visit to Anfield in 20 years in March 2004. They were defeated by a 91st-minute header from which Reds defender?

553. Ian Rush scored a late winner in what was Graeme Souness' last league game in charge - but who was it against?

554. Who scored the winner in the game in which Kenny Dalglish led his Blackburn side to become Champions despite losing to the Reds in the Anfield game?

555. In possibly the Premier League's greatest match and with the game against Newcastle tied at 3-3 who hit the winner at Anfield in 1996?

556. Who kept goal for Everton when Gary McAllister scored the winner at Goodison Park in April 2001?

557. In March and October 2002 Liverpool beat which club 1-0 with winners scored on 90 minutes?

558. Who in November 2004 completed his only hat-trick for the Reds by converting a penalty which he had himself won?

559. Who in 2004 hammered a winner past Jeans Lehmann in an Anfield encounter with Arsenal - Liverpool winning 2-1?

560. Whose penalty in March 2016 was the club's first ever 96th minute winner in a Premier League game, doing so against the club he later joined?

# DEJAN LOVREN

561. Dejan played in the 2018 World Cup final but suffered defeat against which country?

562. Prior to 2019/20 against which club did he score his only goal in European competition for the Reds?

563. Against which club did he score his first goal for Southampton?

564. Lovren scored his first goal for the Reds with a 90th minute winning header against which team in October 2014?

565. Lovren made his debut for the Reds in August 2014. Who were the opposition that day?

566. Against which club did Lovren miss the fifth and vital penalty in a shootout which saw the Reds eliminated from the Europa League?

567. In January 2018 he captained the Reds for the first time beating which side 4-3?

568. Prior to 2019/20 Dejan's last three goals saw Liverpool win the games all by the same score - what was it?

569. Which player opposed Lovren in the Champions League final and was then a teammate of his in the World Cup final?

570. Who was his central defender partner in the 2016 Europa League final?

# WORLD CUP

571. Which former Southampton defender scored for England at the 1990 World Cup against Egypt?

572. Prior to Dejan Lovren who was the previous, then current, Liverpool player to appear in a World Cup final?

573. Which Liverpool player has scored four goals in the World Cup Final Stages?

574. Who having scored in the 1974 Finals then scored as a Reds player in the 1978 tournament?

575. Who was the only Liverpool player to appear for England in the 2014 and 2018 Finals?

576. After the 2002 Finals, two players from the same nation made their debuts for the Reds in August. Which country was this?

577. Which Red scored in the 1990 penalty shootout against Germany?

578. And which future Liverpool player was successful with his penalty in that shootout for Germany?

579. Which player in 2018 scored for Belgium against England in the Third place Play-Off and against Liverpool in the opening game of the Champions League Group Stages?

580. Which Liverpool player was in his country's World Cup squads in both 2014 and 2018 but failed to make an appearance?

# JOEL MATIP

581. Against which club in 2018 did Joel score the first Anfield goal of his Liverpool career?

582. For which country had he played international football?

583. In which country was Joel born?

584. It took him 98 matches before he got his first assist as a player, doing so against which club?

585. In 2010/11 Matip came on as a substitute in the Champions League semi-final whilst playing for which club?

586. In October 2016 the defender scored his first Liverpool goal doing so in a 4-2 defeat of which club?

587. Prior to the 2019/20 season Matip had scored the same number of goals in each of the last three seasons. How many was this?

588. In January 2018 the defender scored his first own goal in a Reds shirt doing so against which club?

589. Matip's 2018/19 campaign was interrupted when he suffered a broken collarbone whilst playing against which club?

590. Playing against which club did Matip score an equalising goal in the 2014 World Cup, although he finished on the losing side?

# DEFENDERS

591. Whose only Champions League goal for the Reds came in a 1-0 semi-final second leg victory at Anfield in 2007?

592. Which full-back went in goal as an emergency in the league game at Newcastle in 2012?

593. Which defender took over the goalkeeper's duties in the game with Everton in 1999?

594. Liverpool took a 1-0 lead to Leverkusen in the Champions League quarter-final in 2002 when which man scored the only goal of the game?

595. In July 2005 who scored his first Liverpool goal in six years to put his side 2-1 up against Kaunas?

596. Who scored an own goal whilst with Wimbledon against Liverpool in 1993, and was in the Reds' 1996 FA Cup final side?

597. Which full-back was sent-off for the only time in his short Liverpool career in a 2-0 win at Charlton in October 2001?

598. Despite his defending, he is often remembered for a celebrated televised hat-trick at Newcastle - who is he?

599. Against France in 1992, Alan Shearer began his long England career. Which Liverpool player also made his debut in the game?

600. Who holds the club record of playing over 400 consecutive games for Liverpool?

601. On his Liverpool debut, which Stoke City striker had an 89th-minute penalty saved by Mignolet?

602. After six years at Anfield, Simon returned to his homeland to join which club?

603. Which Liverpool player missed a penalty against Mignolet's Sunderland side in 2011?

604. After being left out following a Champions League game in December 2014, who took Simon's place only to be injured on Boxing Day?

605. Against which club did he concede the most goals in a Premier League game in his time with the Reds?

606. Liverpool used three goalkeepers in the 2017/18 season, Mignolet and Loris Karius were two. Who was the other?

607. The Belgian saved a 90th-minute penalty in March 2015 from which England international?

608. He captained the Reds for the first time in November 2017 in a 4-1 defeat of which club?

609. Against which club did he make the last of 204 appearances in a Reds shirt in all competitions?

610. In the 2016 League Cup semi-final shoot-out, Mignolet saved a penalty from which former Liverpool player?

# PREMIER LEAGUE

611. Who kept goal for the club in their first Premiership game at Nottingham Forest in 1992?

612. Which former Liverpool goalkeeper never played for them in the Premiership, but conceded five at Anfield while playing for Fulham?

613. By the end of the 2018/19 season, which Liverpool player had appeared as a substitute in the Premier League on most occasions?

614. Against which club in 1998 did Michael Owen become Liverpool's youngest hat-trick scorer in the Premier League?

615. Which player appeared in a record 38 Premier League games against the Reds?

616. Which of Liverpool's many overseas internationals has scored the most goals in the Premier League for them, prior to the start of the 2019/20 campaign?

617. With which club was David Burrows playing, when he scored an own-goal in a game against Liverpool in March 1995?

618. For which club have Adam Tanner and Marcus Stewart scored winning goals against Liverpool?

619. In the first six weeks of the Premiership in 1992, which player scored three penalties?

620. Who in April 2003 scored his second Premier League penalty against the Reds in the Merseyside derby?

# ALBERTO MORENO

621. From which club did Liverpool sign the Spanish defender in August 2014?

622. In the same month he signed, he was joined by which fellow Spaniard who moved to Anfield on loan from Atletico Madrid?

623. Which manager gave Alberto his league debut in a game at Manchester City?

624. Moreno started the 2015/16 season on the bench, but soon replaced which injured full-back before playing 50 games in all competitions?

625. In 2014, he played in a winning Europa League final under which manager?

626. Who was his teammate in that 2014 final who played in midfield against the Reds in the 2019 Champions League semi-final?

627. The full-back played in a 7-0 Anfield demolition of which side in December 2017, before injury caused him to lose his place?

628. Brendan Rodgers' 100th Liverpool match, Mario Balotelli's debut and Moreno netting his first Liverpool goal, all came against which team in August 2014?

629. Moreno's last game for the club saw him play in a 2-1 defeat at which club in January 2019?

630. Alberto's third and final goal for Liverpool gave the Reds an eighth-minute lead as they won 4-1 against which side in April 2016?

# SPANISH CONNECTION

631. After 141 games for the Reds, which Spanish club did Alberto Moreno join in July 2019?

632. Who was the first Spanish international to play for Liverpool after having won the Champions League with another club?

633. Who was the first Liverpool player to leave Anfield and go on to win the Champions League?

634. Which former Red missed a penalty for Spain as they crashed out of the 2018 World Cup against Russia?

635. Against which side did Xabi Alonso score from 65 yards in a FA Cup match?

636. Who played for Manchester City while on loan from Espanyol and scored five goals in his Anfield career before having a short spell with Watford?

637. Against which club did Luis Garcia score a goal in the 109th minute of a game in Monaco in 2005?

638. Which defender failed to make a single appearance for the Reds in his three years at Anfield, but while back in his homeland made his Spanish international debut in 2014?

639. In 1968/69, Liverpool lost on the toss of a coin and were knocked out of the Fairs Cup by which club?

640. Which former Red managed Xabi Alonso at Real Sociedad?

# MICHAEL OWEN

641. Michael famously scored against Argentina in the 1998 World Cup, but which other player was also on the scoresheet for England?

642. Against which country did Owen score an England hat-trick in September 2001?

643. His first two league goals came in different seasons, both against Wimbledon at which ground?

644. It took him just six minutes to score on his European club debut when scoring in a 2-2 draw against which club?

645. His last goal for Liverpool came in May 2004 against a club he would later play for. Which club was it?

646. Two of his most important goals came in the UEFA Cup fourth round in 2001 when the Reds defeated which side 2-0 in the away leg?

647. For which club did Michael score his 150th and last Premier League goal?

648. With Liverpool 4-3 up against Alaves, Michael was replaced by which player in the UEFA Cup final?

649. Who was the former Liverpool player who as youth development officer persuaded the youngster to join the Anfield youth set-up?

650. When Real Madrid signed Owen in August 2004, which player moved to Anfield as a makeweight in the deal?

# ENGLAND INTERNATIONALS

651. Who played for the Reds in the 2018/19 season having won 61 England caps, with only seven coming in his time at Anfield?

652. When Michael Owen hit his hat-trick for England in 2001, Steven Gerrard and which other Liverpool player was also on the scoresheet?

653. In the 2014 World Cup Finals, against which country did Daniel Sturridge score England's goal in a 2-1 defeat?

654. With which club did Kevin Keegan win his last nine England caps?

655. Which Liverpool player played in five of England's World Cup games in the 1990 Finals, but missed the semi-final through injury?

656. Who was the first Liverpool player to appear in a World Cup final?

657. In 2006, which striker set an English record with eleven goals in a calendar year, a total that included a hat-trick against Jamaica at Old Trafford?

658. England played five matches in Euro'96 in their own country. Which Liverpool player appeared in all of those games?

659. Which midfielder scored on his debut for England in a 2-1 win against Wales at Wrexham in 1976?

660. Who won exactly 50 caps for his country while at Anfield, scoring five goals?

# ALEX OXLADE-CHAMBERLAIN

661. Prior to moving to Anfield, Alex scored in a 4-3 defeat to which club on the opening day of the 2016/17 season?

662. What was the transfer fee paid by Liverpool to Arsenal to secure his services?

663. Against which club did he make his first appearance in a Red shirt, coming on as a substitute in a 5-0 defeat?

664. His first goal came in October 2017, latching onto a Daniel Sturridge pass to score Liverpool's sixth of seven goals in Slovenia. Who were Liverpool's opponents?

665. Who was his former teammate that he scored against in the 5-0 Anfield defeat of Swansea in December 2017?

666. Alex returned to the fray after serious injury in April 2019, coming on as a substitute in the 5-0 Anfield defeat of which club?

667. Which England manager gave him his first major international tournament debut?

668. In June 2013, Alex scored in a 1-1 draw against the country where his father and John Barnes had starred in 1984. Which country was this?

669. Who kept goal for Liverpool when Ox scored in the 2-1 defeat of the Reds in the FA Cup in 2014?

670. Which was the first side he scored against in two different competitions in the same season for the Reds?

671. Alex Oxlade-Chamberlain's father Mark won his eight England caps while playing for which club?

672. Mark played with a centre-forward in 1984, whose father had scored 27 times for Liverpool in 1967/68. Who was the striker?

673. What is the surname of Roy and Dean, who made post-war Liverpool appearances?

674. His grandfather played in the 1950 FA Cup final and he himself went on to play 243 times for Liverpool. Who is this defender?

675. This Liverpool defender made nine appearances for Liverpool, and his brother scored Everton's winner in the 1991 FA Cup fifth round second replay against the Reds. Who is he?

676. The son of which 1977 European Cup winner played against Liverpool for Tottenham and Birmingham?

677. The father of which Liverpool striker of the Nineties managed two different clubs to League Championship wins in the 1970s?

678. Which former Liverpool captain's son played against the Reds for Crystal Palace, Derby County and Huddersfield Town between 2014-18?

679. Which pair of brothers played against Liverpool in the 1977 FA Cup final?

680. The son of which Premier League winner helped his side beat Liverpool in February 2016 en route to winning the Premier League himself?

# JAMIE REDKNAPP

681. Whilst managing which club, did his father Harry, give the youngster his league debut?

682. Jamie was signed by which Liverpool manager?

683. He became the then youngest Liverpool player ever to make a European debut, doing so against which French club in 1991?

684. Which manager in 1995 gave Redknapp his first England cap in a goalless draw at Wembley?

685. In that debut against Columbia, it was the debutant's cross that gave which goalkeeper the chance to perform his scorpion kick?

686. His first goal in a Reds shirt came against a side he also later played for. Which side was it?

687. Who did Jamie replace as Liverpool captain?

688. His last Liverpool goal came in a 2-0 victory at which London club?

689. In January 1995, the future pundit scored in a 1-1 FA Cup draw, and then again in the subsequent shoot-out against which club?

690. Which was the only major trophy he won with Liverpool in which he played?

# PUNDITS

691. Which player once scored in the first nine games of a league season?

692. Who was the first Liverpool player to score from a penalty in the Charity Shield?

693. Which pundit became Bob Paisley's last signing as manager in May 1983?

694. Name the Premier League player, who after leaving Liverpool, appeared for Aston Villa, Fulham, Leicester City, Bradford City and Real Oviedo?

695. Who made his Liverpool debut as a substitute against Sheffield United under Kenny Dalglish and was awarded his first start under Graeme Souness?

696. Which forward scored 13 goals in 52 Liverpool appearances, was part of the 1983/84 treble-winning season and later became a Spanish TV presenter?

697. Who was a member of the Reds title-winning squad of 1987/88 and later managed Sheffield United, Barnsley and Millwall?

698. Which manager bought Istvan Kozma from Dunfermline and Paul Stewart from Tottenham?

699. Which England international began his career with Crewe Alexandra and ended it with Blackburn?

700. Which future pundit scored 14 times for the Reds against Newcastle United?

# PEPE REINA

701. In September 2012 Pepe was sent-off for the second time in his Liverpool career in a 2-0 defeat at which club?

702. Against which team did he concede his first ever goal at Anfield doing so in a European competition?

703. From which club did the Reds sign the Spanish International?

704. How many penalties did he save in the 2006 FA Cup final?

705. And in that game's shoot-out which future Red was the second player to be thwarted by Pepe?

706. Which goalkeeper kept Reina out of the Spanish side which won both the European Championship and World Cup?

707. When missing seven games in the 2012/13 season which keeper deputised for him making seven of his 11 Liverpool career appearances?

708. Which manager took Pepe to Italy in May 2013?

709. Pepe's father also played in a losing European Cup final, doing so in 1974 when Bayern Munich defeated which side?

710. In August 2010 the goalkeeper was responsible for the Reds dropping points with his own goal in the last minute in a 1-1 draw with which club?

# SENDINGS OFF

711. Against which club did Liverpool win 3-2 in March 1998, the hosts finishing the game with eight men as Steve McManaman scored a last minute winner?

712. In Liverpool's 3-2 win at Goodison in the treble winning season of 2000/01, which player was red carded with the Reds leading 2-1?

713. In Liverpool's first win at Stamford Bridge since 1989, which Liverpool player was dismissed after 87 minutes?

714. In a derby played in December 2005 who were the two Evertonians sent-off?

715. Against which team were both Charlie Adam and Martin Skrtel sent-off in 2011 - a game which Liverpool lost 4-0?

716. Name the Reds forward sent-off three times in six years during the 1960s?

717. Who was red-carded at West Ham in April 2006 - a dismissal that ruled him out of Liverpool's FA Cup final?

718. Two Reds players were dismissed deep into injury time of a UEFA Cup tie in Spain in 1998. Paul Ince was one, who was the other?

719. Emile Heskey and Peter Crouch have both been red carded in the 2000s in League Cup ties against the same team. Which team?

720. Which club had a player sent-off in each leg of a Champions League tie against the Reds in 2007/2008?

# ANDREW ROBERTSON

721. Against which club did Andy score his first goal for Liverpool?

722. And in that game which of his teammates scored his only goal in a Reds shirt?

723. After suffering relegation he left which club to join Liverpool?

724. The Scot played for which club before his move into English football?

725. Against which club in April 2019 did Andy's crosses lead to goals for Sadio Mane and Mo Salah?

726. Which player's foul on the Scot in the Champions League semi-final forced Robertson off at half-time?

727. Which manager gave Andy his Scotland debut against Poland in March 2014?

728. His first goal for his country, sadly for him, saw Scotland defeated 3-1 by which country?

729. In June 2019 he scored the opening goal as Scotland beat Cyprus at the ground where he once played league football - which ground was this?

730. The Scot's Premier League debut came in a 1-0 win against which club in August 2017 that saw him win many plaudits for his performance?

# THE SCOTTISH CONNECTION

731. Which player scored the winning goal when Liverpool won at Goodison Park for the first time in a Premier League visit?

732. Which former Red scored in Stoke's 5-3 loss to, and the 6-1 defeat of Liverpool at the Britannia Stadium?

733. Which player came to Anfield in 1981 and was Liverpool's only player in Scotland's 1986 World Cup squad?

734. Who was the last Scot to lift the European Cup as captain?

735. Who played in the Merseyside derby for both sides after his move to Anfield from Hartlepool United?

736. Who captained the Reds to their first FA Cup final win?

737. Who was the only Liverpool player to appear in any squad at the 1974 World Cup?

738. When Liverpool clinched the League title at Stamford Bridge in 1986 two future Liverpool players were in the opposition. Nigel Spackman was one. Name the other?

739. Which goalkeeper won just three caps for Scotland in the Sixties?

740. Which defender netted a rare hat-trick in Liverpool's 5-0 defeat of Birmingham City at Anfield in 1986?

741. From which club did Liverpool sign the youngster for a fee of around £300,000?

742. Against which club did he score four of his five FA Cup final goals?

743. In what year was he appointed Liverpool captain?

744. In November 1994, Rush celebrated his 600th senior Liverpool appearance by scoring a League Cup hat trick against which club?

745. In the Championship-winning season of 1989/90, Rush finished second in Liverpool's goalscoring list to which player?

746. In October 1992, Rush scored his record-breaking goal for the club which took him past which 1960s legend?

747. Who managed Ian Rush in his last game for Liverpool?

748. Which player scored in the 1992 FA Cup final and then played the pass from which Rush grabbed the second?

749. The first time Ian scored for the club and ended up on the losing side came six years after his debut. Who was it against?

750. In 1996, Rush made his last appearance for the Reds when he came on as a substitute for which player in the FA Cup final?

# THE WELSH CONNECTION

751. Who in 2012 became the first player in over 50 years to join Liverpool from Swansea?

752. Which team did Liverpool beat in their first League Cup final at the Millennium Stadium?

753. Who was the Welsh international who came on as a substitute in the 2012 League Cup final defeat of Cardiff City?

754. Who moved from Derby County and also played under Graeme Souness at Galatasaray and Benfica?

755. Which future Welsh team manager was in the Swansea side beaten 8-0 by the Reds in an FA Cup reply in 1990?

756. Which youngster came on for Philippe Coutinho at Plymouth in the FA Cup in 2017 to make his club debut?

757. Which goalkeeper played his only two games for Liverpool in 2004 when Chris Kirkland and Jerzy Dudek were both injured?

758. Who was the first Welshman to win a European Cup final with the Reds?

759. In the shoot-out with Cardiff in the 2012 League Cup final, the cousin of which Liverpool player missed the decisive penalty?

760. Who scored 96 goals for Liverpool and played for both Cardiff and Swansea?

# MOHAMED SALAH

761. Against which club did Mo become the first player in over four years to score four times for Liverpool in a Premier League fixture?

762. In December 2018, after scoring a hat-trick at Bournemouth, Salah gave his match ball to which teammate?

763. Against which club did the forward score the goal which won him the 2018 FIFA Puskas award for the best goal scored between July 2017 and July 2018?

764. Whose previous record did he surpass in 2017/18 for the most goals scored in a debut season for the Reds?

765. Against which club did he first play in a winning side in the Premier League at Anfield?

766. In November 2017, Jurgen Klopp kept the Egyptian on the bench only for him to score twice against which club in his 23 minutes on the pitch?

767. How many goals did Salah score in the 2017/18 league season which earned him the Golden Boot?

768. On which ground did Mo score in a 4-0 win in December 2017 and then three times on his next visit, also in a 4-0 victory?

769. Salah in 2018 broke whose club record of nine goals scored in a single European campaign?

770. For which club did Salah score against both Tottenham and Chelsea in the same European campaign?

# HAT-TRICKS

771. Which player once scored five goals in only his fourth game for the club?

772. Who was the first hat-trick scorer for the Reds in an away Premier League game, doing so in a 3-3 draw at Hillsborough?

773. Which legendary player scored a stunning 241 goals in 377 games which included a record 17 hat-tricks for the Reds?

774. Who scored the club's first Premier League hat-trick in April 1993?

775. Name the Everton goalkeeper beaten four times by Ian Rush in the league at Goodison in November 1982?

776. Kenny Dalglish scored three hat-tricks during his distinguished Reds career. Two were scored against which club?

777. In January 2008, Steven Gerrard became the first Liverpool player to score three times in a FA Cup tie since which man in 1996?

778. Who scored a 28th-second opener and two penalties for Southampton against the Reds at The Dell in 1994?

779. In a League Cup tie in October 1989, who scored a hat-trick at Anfield for the Reds with Liverpool playing as the away team?

780. Who in January 2007 became the first visiting player to score four goals in a game at Anfield since Dennis Westcott in 1946?

# XHERDAN SHAQIRI

781. Against which club did Shaqiri score his first goal for Liverpool in a 4-1 Anfield win?

782. The Swiss star quickly became a hero when he scored a spectacular scissor-kick in a pre-season friendly in 2018, against which club?

783. Prior to 'Shaq's' move to Anfield, who was the previous Swiss international to appear in a league game for the club?

784. The player scored a wonderful cushioned goal against Fulham in November 2018, netting from whose cross?

785. In September 2018, a 25-yard free-kick from Xherdan hit the crossbar, which allowed Mo Salah to tap home against which club?

786. Against which team was he left out of a Liverpool Champions League game for safety reasons?

787. As a result of a ball he played into the Southampton box at Anfield in 2018, which player scored an own-goal?

788. Prior to his Anfield move, Shaqiri was an unused substitute in the 2013 Champions League final while with which club?

789. For which club did he play for five seasons from 2007-2012?

790. Against which country did he score a 2014 World Cup hat-trick?

# INTERNATIONALS

791. Only two players whose surnames begin with the letter I have played for England since World War II, and both played for Liverpool. Who are they?

792. Who made over 100 appearances for his country and left Anfield in August 2018 to join Cagliari?

793. Against which country did Michael Owen score an England hat-trick in September 2001?

794. Who won exactly 50 caps for his country while at Anfield, scoring five goals?

795. England played five matches in Euro'96 in their own country. Which Liverpool player appeared in all of those games?

796. Which Liverpool legend came to Anfield in the 1977/78 season from Partick Thistle?

797. Who is Liverpool's most capped Norwegian with 110 caps, winning 64 with the Reds?

798. Two Finnish international players won caps while playing for the Reds, one was Sami Hyypia, who was the other?

799. Two Liverpool players have won international caps for Croatia, Dejan Lovren and who else?

800. Who played for Scotland on 29 occasions between 1946 and 1955?

# MARTIN SKRTEL

801. Against which club did Martin score for both sides in 2010, and get sent-off the following year on the same ground?

802. For which country did Skrtel make over 100 international appearances?

803. His first start in a Reds shirt saw him score an own-goal in a 5-2 defeat of which non-league side?

804. In August 2012, he opened the scoring against Manchester City in a 2-2 draw at Anfield, but who scored an equaliser after a careless back-pass by Martin?

805. After an eight years at Anfield, he ended his association with the Reds and joined which club?

806. Against which club in October 2008 did Skrtel suffer an injury which saw him miss the following two months?

807. The defender scored only one Cup goal in his Anfield career, doing so against which club?

808. Against which club did he score twice in the first ten minutes of a game which saw Liverpool win 5-1 at Anfield?

809. From which club did Liverpool sign the defender during the 2008 January transfer window?

810. In January 2015, which Chelsea forward escaped retrospective action having stamped on Skrtel?

# THE TOTTENHAM CONNECTION

811. Which player in 2018/19 both missed and then converted a penalty?

812. Which player during the 1998/99 season scored an own-goal in both league encounters?

813. Tottenham secured their first Premier League win at Anfield in August 1993 when which player scored both goals in a 2-1 win?

814. Which player moved from White Hart Lane in July 2008 and scored seven times for the Reds before returning to Tottenham six months later?

815. Who is the only goalkeeper to play for both sides in the Premier League?

816. Jurgen Klopp's first game in charge of Liverpool came at Spurs in October 2015. Who captained the Reds that day?

817. Which defender scored his only Liverpool goal in the 5-0 win at White Hart Lane in 2013?

818. Tottenham's biggest win over the Reds came in April 1963 when which legendary figure scored four times?

819. En route to the 1971 FA Cup final, which player scored the winning goal in a sixth round replay at White Hart Lane?

820. Who in September 1974 scored his only hat-trick for Liverpool, doing so against Spurs?

# VLADIMIR SMICER

821. Smicer came on for which player after just 23 minutes in Istanbul to score Liverpool's second goal?

822. With which club did he win the French League prior to his Anfield transfer?

823. Which of Vladi's teammates scored his country's only goal in the Euro '96 final?

824. Injury prevented him from playing for his new club at Anfield in the 2006/07 Champions League. Which club had he joined?

825. The Czech scored his only goal in the FA Cup, a penalty in the fifth round in 2001, against which club?

826. One of his finest goals came in March 2002 when his late strike beat which Chelsea goalkeeper?

827. His first goal in the League Cup came in the 8-0 victory at which ground?

828. Smicer scored in both games of the 2001 League Cup semi-final against which club?

829. In 2002, Smicer came on as a substitute against which club in the Community Shield, when he picked up a rare losers medal?

830. Prior to joining the Reds, he appeared at Anfield for his national team. The Czech Republic played Euro '96 group games in front of the Kop against Italy, and which country?

# SUBSTITUTES

831. Which player ended his Reds career with a club record ten Premier League goals in 45 substitute appearances?

832. Which Liverpool substitute was sent-off against Everton in 1999 and Manchester United in 2015?

833. Who scored an equaliser just two minutes after coming on as a half-time substitute against Olympiakos in the Champions League in 2004 to level the score?

834. Prior to 2019/20 who was the last Liverpool substitute to be substituted in a game on two occasions?

835. Ian Rush came on as a substitute in the 1989 FA Cup final, replacing which man?

836. Which player came on for England and had to be taken off through injury against Scotland in Euro '96?

837. Who was himself replaced after coming on in a European Cup semi-final in 1981?

838. Who was the first substitute to score a hat-trick for the Reds?

839. Which man was the only Reds substitute to score twice in a Premier League game in 2018/19?

840. Who was Liverpool's first-ever substitute in league football, replacing Chris Lawler?

# DANIEL STURRIDGE

841. Daniel's 50th league goal for the club came against Chelsea, but against which club did he get his first?

842. Sturridge scored just 24 seconds after coming on as a substitute in August 2018, against which club?

843. He moved to Anfield from Chelsea, but at which club did he begin his career?

844. When the striker scored at Swansea in 2013 to equalise after just four minutes, which former Red put a back-pass into his path?

845. The England striker scored five times against Aston Villa, scoring four times past which goalkeeper?

846. Sturridge scored three times in the 2015/16 Europa League campaign, against Villarreal, Sevilla and which other team?

847. In May 2017, Daniel scored Liverpool's first-ever goal at London Stadium, placing his shot past which goalkeeper?

848. Against which club did Daniel score in two competitions in September 2018?

849. The player left Anfield in 2019 and joined a club the Reds had played in the European Cup in 1976. Which club was this?

850. Sturridge famously scored in each of his first three appearances for Liverpool, equalling the feat of which future England star in 1974?

# MANCHESTER CITY

851. Which former City player's only goal for Liverpool against City came in a 2-2 draw at the Etihad in February 2013?

852. Which Liverpool player scored against his former club with a penalty in the 1-1 draw at the Etihad in March 2017?

853. Who made his Liverpool debut as a substitute at City in the 5-0 loss in September 2017, and later that season scored in the Anfield league and Champions League wins?

854. Who was the first Manchester City player since Tony Book in 1967 to miss a penalty against the Reds?

855. Which former World Player of the Year has scored for both City and Chelsea against the Reds in the Premier League?

856. Which Liverpool player scored two penalties in a Maine Road win in March 1991?

857. Who scored his last goal for the Reds in the 2-2 draw in Manchester in May 1996?

858. In the 2-2 draw at City in December 2003, two former Reds scored for the hosts - Nicolas Anelka and who else?

859. In the two games at Anfield in two competitions in October 1995, how many goals did City concede?

860. City won at Anfield for the first time since 1953 on Boxing Day 1981 when which son of the manager scored in a 3-1 win?

# LUIS SUAREZ

861. From which club did Liverpool sign the Uruguayan?

862. Suarez endeared himself to the Kop when he scored on his debut against which club?

863. A red card issued to Suarez prevented him from playing in the World Cup semi-final of 2010. Against which country was he dismissed?

864. Suarez scored his first Wembley goal in 2012, capitalising on which Evertonian's mistake?

865. He captained the club for the first time in January 2013. It was not a happy occasion as the Reds were beaten 3-2 at which lower league club?

866. Against which club did he play his last game for Liverpool in 2014?

867. Suarez scored for Liverpool in a 2-1 home defeat to Wigan Athletic in March 2012. Which future England international made his debut in the game?

868. His last goal saw Liverpool take a 3-0 lead over which club in May 2014, only for them to drop two points?

869. Suarez captained Uruguay during the 2012 Olympics, but suffered a 1-0 loss to Great Britain with a goal from which Chelsea striker?

870. Which England goalkeeper was beaten twice by the Uruguayan in his country's 2-1 win at the 2014 World Cup?

# OVERSEAS INTERNATIONALS

871. Prior to the start of the 2019/20 season, who had scored more Premier League goals against Liverpool than any other overseas player?

872. When Chelsea beat Liverpool in 3-1 at Anfield in the Champions League in April 2009, which player scored the visitors' first two goals?

873. For which club did Ramires, David Luiz and Angel Di Maria all play against the Reds in Europe in 2010?

874. Who started the 2011/12 season in a Reds shirt and ended the campaign playing against Liverpool in the FA Cup final?

875. Who played for Manchester United in the Champions League final of 1999, and for AC Milan against Liverpool in Istanbul?

876. Within days of their 2-0 defeat to Liverpool in April 2003, which former French international was relieved of his managerial duties at Fulham?

877. Who captained Spain to victory in the 2008 European Championships and played against Liverpool in the Champions League in 2018/19?

878. Who scored a goal to help knock England out of the World Cup in 2002 and then scored against Liverpool at Anfield in the Champions League run in 2004?

879. Who won the Champions League in 1996 and later that year scored a hat-trick against Liverpool on his Premier League debut?

880. For which team was Delfi Geli playing when he scored a history-making own-goal?

881. Which international made the last of his 534 games for Liverpool against Southampton in August 1960?

882. In 1964, the BBC cameras covered a Liverpool home game for the first-ever Match of the Day programme. Who were their opponents?

883. In December 1967, which opposition goalkeeper, in attempting to clear the ball, inexplicably threw the ball into his own net?

884. Tony Hateley scored 27 times for Liverpool in his debut season before moving to which club?

885. Three Liverpool players were in England's 22-man World Cup-winning squad in 1966. Which of the three made just one appearance?

886. Which 2019/20 Championship team were Liverpool's first-ever opponents in the League Cup, back in 1960?

887. Liverpool used 14 players in winning the title in the 1965/66 season, but which of those made just one appearance?

888. The Reds broke their transfer record in 1967, spending £65,000 to secure the services of which player?

889. Who was the Leicester City goalkeeper, who kept a clean sheet against the Reds in the FA Cup semi-final in 1963, who played the last game of his professional career at Anfield nine years later?

890. The first time Liverpool faced Swedish opposition in European competition was in the 1967/68 Fairs Cup. Who did they play?

# THE 1970s

891. Who scored Liverpool's winning goal in the 1976 Charity Shield against Southampton?

892. Against which team did Ian Callaghan score three goals in a game for the only time in a Reds shirt, in a League Cup tie in 1973?

893. When Liverpool met Leicester in the 1971 Charity Shield, on which ground was the game staged?

894. Which player did Bob Paisley sign for the club for £352,000, completing the transfer in an empty Leeds ballroom?

895. Away to which team did Liverpool lose an FA Cup tie in 1975, but returned to the same ground to knock-out the holders four years later in the sixth round?

896. In 1974, Kevin Keegan's suspension led to which replacement scoring nine times before the end of September?

897. Who was Liverpool's substitute goalkeeper in each of their European Cup games in 1976/77, though he never made an appearance?

898. In the unforgettable league season of 1978/79, Liverpool conceded a miserly 16 goals. How many of those were scored at Anfield?

899. Which Everton player had the unfortunate distinction of scoring an own-goal after just 35 seconds in the 4-0 defeat at Anfield in 1972?

900. Liverpool's record European attendance at Anfield was set in 1976. 55,104 watched the encounter with which team?

# PHIL THOMPSON

901. 'Tommo' captained Liverpool to their first League Cup final win when they beat which team 2-1?

902. One of his most celebrated goals saw the Reds draw 1-1 with which side in the 1976 UEFA Cup semi-final?

903. In which city did the defender captain his club to a European Cup final win?

904. Which England player did he replace at the heart of the Liverpool defence in the 1970s with Tommy Smith moving to full-back?

905. In the 1974 FA Cup final, which England forward did 'Tommo' mark out of the game?

906. Against which country in May 1976 did he score his only goal for England?

907. He was adjudged to have fouled which player, albeit outside the box, which resulted in Nottingham Forest's League Cup final winner from the penalty spot in 1978?

908. After leaving Anfield, the defender made 37 league appearances for which Division Two side?

909. His last European goal came in the 6-0 defeat of which club?

910. He made his debut for the Reds as a substitute for which forward as Liverpool beat Manchester United in 1972?

# LIVERPOOL CUP CAMPAIGNS

911. Which player scored against three Premier League sides in the Champions League in 2018/19, including two against the Reds?

912. Who scored after just 43 seconds in a League Cup final for Liverpool?

913. Which club have Liverpool been drawn against most often in the League Cup?

914. Who is the only Manchester United player to score against the Reds in European competition?

915. Kenny Dalglish in 1984 and Ryan Babel were sent-off when playing against which club in European games?

916. Which club knocked the Reds out of the FA Cup in both 1990 and 2003?

917. Which player between 1981-1995, played in 42 League Cup games for Liverpool, but never in a final?

918. Seven different players scored in the 10-0 defeat of which Irish side in 1969?

919. The 2018/19 Champ[ions League campaign saw Liverpool meet which team in European competition for the first time in 46 years?

920. Guy Whittingham played in two FA Cup semi-finals against Liverpool, doing so for Portsmouth and which other club?

# KOLO TOURE

921. After his time at Anfield, at which club was he reunited with Brendan Rodgers as a player?

922. For which country did he play his international football?

923. Against which club did the defender play his last game in a red shirt?

924. In that game, he was replaced after 83 minutes by which forward?

925. Against which team, in a European game in 2015, did Toure captain Liverpool for the first time?

926. Against which club In February 2014, did Kolo score an own-goal as early as the eighth minute, although the Reds won the game 3-2?

927. Earlier in February 2014, which player took advantage of Toure's mistake to equalise in a 1-1 draw at the Hawthorns?

928. Against which club did Toure score for the Reds in a 6-0 win?

929. At which ground did Kolo make his debut in English football for Arsenal?

930. What number shirt did he wear in both his first and last appearance for Liverpool?

# THE OLD FIRM CONNECTION

931. Like Kolo Toure, which Welsh international played for Manchester City, Liverpool and Celtic?

932. Who is the only man to manage Liverpool and Rangers?

933. Kenny Dalglish and who else played for Liverpool before managing Celtic?

934. Who scored for Bolton in the 1995 League Cup final and then for Celtic in the UEFA Cup tie at Anfield eight years later?

935. Which Celtic legend scored against the Reds at Celtic Park in that UEFA Cup season, before scoring twice in the final?

936. Which defender played for Rangers and was sent-off in the Merseyside derby in 2010 after tangling with Marouane Fellaini?

937. Prior to 2019/20, who was the last player to appear in the Champions League with both Celtic and Liverpool?

938. Whose late goal gave the Reds a 2-2 draw at Celtic Park, which proved decisive with Liverpool winning on away goals?

939. Who played for Liverpool after leaving Ibrox, before appearing for Stoke, Wolves, Southampton and Swindon among others?

940. Which player left Ibrox in 1962 and won the league and FA Cup with Liverpool?

941. Virgil memorably scored a debut-winner against Everton in the FA Cup, when heading home which player's corner?

942. On a Friday night in December 2018, the defender scored his club's second goal in a 2-0 win at which ground?

943. With which club did he play in the Champions League before doing so with the Reds?

944. After Virgil van Dijk made his Reds debut in January 2018, he was then left out of the next game. Who were Liverpool's opponents?

945. He scored twice for the club for the first time in the 5-0 defeat of which side in February 2019?

946. Virgil captained Liverpool for the first time as the Reds beat which team at Anfield in the Champions League in 2018?

947. Who is Virgil's former teammate who scored against Liverpool on the opening day of the 2019/20 league season?

948. In December 2015, van Dijk played in a League Cup tie which saw Liverpool win 6-1, despite which player scoring in the first minute for his club?

949. Who has managed van Dijk at both club and international level?

950. How many goals did van Dijk score in his first full season at Anfield?

# AWARDS

951. Prior to Virgil van Dijk, who was the last Liverpool player to be awarded the PFA Players' Player of the Year?

952. Who in 2013/14 became the first non-European to win the PFA award?

953. Which Liverpool player won the PFA Young Player of the Year award in 2001?

954. Who was the first Liverpool player to win the Football Writers' award on two occasions?

955. The Writers' Footballer of the Year award started in 1948, but who was the first Liverpool player to receive it 26 years later?

956. Who in 1989 was the last Liverpool Scot to be the Writers' Player of the Year?

957. Which Liverpool player won the PFA. Young Player of the Year in successive years, but never won either of the main awards?

958. Who won the PFA award with Ipswich, but not with the Reds?

959. Which player was the Young Player of the Year In 1984 before joining Liverpool, where he scored 37 goals in 112 appearances?

960. Who was the first Liverpool player to win both the PFA and Writers' awards in the same year?

# RONNIE WHELAN

961. Against which club did he score twice in a League Cup final?

962. Ronnie took the position and shirt number of which player?

963. Who managed the Irish international in his last season with Liverpool?

964. Who managed the Irish national side in his two World Cups?

965. Against which club did score on his Liverpool debut in 1981?

966. Against which club did he score in the 1983 League Cup final and the 1985 FA Cup semi-final?

967. In 1992, Whelan scored a dramatic late equaliser at Highbury in the FA Cup semi-final against which club?

968. Against which country did Whelan score a spectacular goal in the 1988 European Championships?

969. After his Anfield career ended, the player moved to which club in 1994?

970. From which Dublin outfit did Liverpool sign Whelan in 1979?

# THE IRISH CONNECTION

971. Who captained Liverpool to their FA Cup final win in 1989?

972. Who played against Liverpool in a League Cup final and the following year in the 1996 FA Cup final for the Reds?

973. Who scored the Irish winner against England in the 1988 European Championships Final Stages?

974. Who was the only Irish International that played in Istanbul against AC Milan, and in that game was replaced by Didi Hamann?

975. Which defender made 31 Republic of Ireland appearances in the 1980s despite being born in Preston?

976. Who played in a Wembley final with Brighton and Queens Park Rangers, while in between, won League and European Cup medals with Liverpool?

977. After leaving Anfield, John Aldridge enjoyed a managerial start with which club?

978. After a short loan period with Queens Park Rangers, which Irishman was sold to Wimbledon for £1.75 million in 1998?

979. Who was the only player to appear in all 13 of Republic of Ireland's matches in the World Cup Finals?

980. Against which country did Jason McAteer and Phil Babb both play in an International at Anfield?

981. From which club did the Reds sign the midfielder?

982. Gini helped the Netherlands to the Euro Nations League final in 2019, only to lose to which country?

983. On which ground did the player score his first away league goal in a Red shirt?

984. He had previously netted in an away game in European football for the Reds when scoring past which goalkeeper?

985. In April 2019, Gini broke the deadlock when he crashed home a Trent Alexander-Arnold corner against which club?

986. Who was the midfielder's teammate in the 2019 European Nations final who had previously scored 22 goals during his Anfield career?

987. Which player replaced Wijnaldum during the Champions League final win against Tottenham Hotspur?

988. Against which club did he open the scoring on the final day of the 2016/17 season, which gained Liverpool a Champions League place for the following campaign?

989. On the last day of 2016, against which side did Gini score the only goal of the game, powerfully heading home an Adam Lallana cross in the eighth minute?

990. September 2018 saw Gini win his 50th international cap, but against which club did he make his 100th outing in a Reds shirt, in a 1-1 away draw?

# MIDFIELDERS

991. Which player began his career at West Ham United and later scored Liverpool's quickest-ever European goal?

992. Which player appeared in a Champions League final with Borussia Dortmund, and scored the two goals which saw Liverpool beat West Brom in the League Cup in September 2012?

993. Which player scored the winning goal at Old Trafford for Liverpool in three different seasons between 2000 and 2004?

994. Which player left Serie A for Anfield in 1997 for a fee of £4million?

995. Which Everton player scored in the first minute of an Anfield 'derby' in April 1999?

996. Name the Liverpool player who was the last man to score a goal in a competitive game at the 'old' Wembley Stadium?

997. Who in 2000/01 became the oldest player to make his League debut for the Reds since World War II?

998. Which Liverpool player appeared in his third European Cup final in 1981, but never won a full England cap?

999. Who scored Liverpool's seventh and final goal in the 7-0 defeat of Tottenham in 1978?

1000. Which member of Liverpool's 2005 European Cup-winning side played for his country at Anfield in Euro '96?

# ANSWERS

## QUIZ 1 · JAMES MILNER

1. Leeds United
2. Brendan Rodgers
3. Seven
4. Arsenal
5. Craig Bellamy
6. Crystal Palace
7. Aston Villa
8. Bordeaux
9. Lukasz Fabianski
10. Alex Oxlade-Chamberlain

## QUIZ 2 · THE 2018/19 SEASON

11. Mo Salah
12. Paris Saint-Germain
13. Lazar Markovic
14. Conor Coady
15. Wolves
16. Watford
17. Daniel Sturridge
18. Eden Hazard
19. Callum Paterson
20. Manchester United

## QUIZ 3 · JORDAN HENDERSON

21. Sunderland

22. Kenny Dalglish (against Sunderland!)
23. Steven Gerrard
24. Newcastle United
25. Alex Ferguson
26. Samir Nasri
27. The Emirates
28. Coventry City
29. Chelsea
30. Wolves

## QUIZ 4 · CAPTAINS

31. Sami Hyypia
32. Ian Rush
33. Emlyn Hughes
34. Alan Hansen
35. Paul Ince
36. Ronnie Moran
37. Tommy Smith
38. Robbie Fowler
39. Jon Flanagan
40. 2015/16

## QUIZ 5 · ALISSON

41. Roma
42. Seven
43. Leicester

44. 21
45. Napoli
46. Wojciech Szczesny
47. Peru
48. No.13
49. All 13
50. Crystal Palace

## QUIZ 6 · GOALKEEPERS

51. Loris Karius
52. Jerzy Dudek
53. Chris Kirkland
54. Pepe Reina
55. Mike Hooper
56. Tommy Lawrence
57. David James
58. Scott Carson
59. Steve Ogrizovic
60. Ned Doig

## QUIZ 7 · SADIO MANE

61. 2016
62. He scored 22
63. Arsenal
64. Daniel Sturridge
65. Porto
66. Red Star Belgrade
67. Watford
68. Dejan Lovren
69. Burnley
70. Joel Robles

## QUIZ 8 · DERBIES

71. Danny Ings
72. Steven Gerrard
73. Daniel Sturridge
74. Sander Westerveld
75. David Johnson
76. Ian Rush
77. Ray Houghton
78. Phil Neal
79. Nick Tanner
80. Abel Xavier

## QUIZ 9 · DIVOCK ORIGI

81. Roberto Firmino
82. Jordan Henderson
83. Wolfsburg
84. Xherdan Shaqiri
85. Red Star Belgrade
86. Virgil Van Dijk
87. St Mary's, Southampton
88. Lille
89. Kenya
90. Ramiro Funes Mori

## QUIZ 10 · CHAMPIONS LEAGUE 2018/19

91. Moussa Sissoko
92. Luis Suarez
93. Napoli
94. Andy Robertson

95. Joel Matip

96. Daniel Sturridge
(also with Chelsea)

97. Porto

98. Pepe

99. Gianluigi Buffon (with
Juventus & Paris St Germain)

100. Alberto Moreno

## QUIZ 11 · FERNANDO TORRES

101. Atletico Madrid

102. Chelsea

103. Rafa Benitez

104. Robbie Fowler

105. West Ham United

106. Germany

107. Tim Howard

108. Real Madrid

109. Ruud van Nistelrooy

110. Molineux, Wolves

## QUIZ 12 · LIVERPOOL V CHELSEA

111. Mo Salah

112. Sander Westerveld

113. Frank Lampard

114. Patrik Berger

115. Joe Cole

116. David Speedie

117. John Arne Riise

118. Jamie Carragher

119. Jonjo Shelvey

120. Dennis Wise

## QUIZ 13 · DANIEL AGGER

121. Brondby

122. West Ham

123. Chelsea

124. West Brom

125. Jamie Carragher

126. Shane Long

127. Newcastle

128. Romania

129. Benfica

130. Manchester United

## QUIZ 14 · CENTRAL DEFENDERS

131. Phil Thompson

132. Sami Hyypia

133. Sunderland

134. Nathan Ake

135. Mark Lawrenson

136. Stephane Henchoz

137. Rotherham United

138. Larry Lloyd

139. Phil Babb

140. Nemanja Vidic

## QUIZ 15 · TRENT ALEXANDER-ARNOLD

141. Watford

142. 66

143. Brazil (Dani Alves and Cafu)

144. Yes - 17 in all competitions

145. Watford

146. Naby Keita

147. Tottenham Hotspur

148. Old Trafford

149. Hoffenheim

150. Switzerland

## QUIZ 16 · LIVERPOOL YOUNGSTERS

151. David Fairclough

152. Ki-Jana Hoever

153. Wimbledon

154. Ben Woodburn

155. Coventry City

156. Harvey Elliott (for Fulham)

157. Sheyi Ojo

158. Curtis Jones

159. Sepp van den Berg

160. Chris Pile

## QUIZ 17 · XABI ALONSO

161. Bayern Munich

162. Chelsea

163. AC Milan (final)

164. Johannesburg

165. Steve Harper

166. Robbie Fowler

167. Eidur Gudjohnsen

168. Jan Kromkamp

169. Chelsea

170. Nigel de Jong

## QUIZ 18 · EUROPEAN CUP CHAMPIONS LEAGUE

171. Basel

172. Dida

173. Hernan Crespo

174. Aberdeen

175. Karim Benzema

176. Red Star Belgrade

177. FC Haka

178. Emmanuel Adebayor

179. Chris Lawler

180. Wissam Ben Yedder

## QUIZ 19 · JOHN BARNES

181. Watford

182. Peter Beardsley

183. David Seaman

184. Steve Ogrizovic

185. Crewe Alexandra

186. Argentina

187. Graham Taylor

188. Sheffield Wednesday

189. Liverpool

190. Sion

## QUIZ 20 · FA CUP

191. James Milner (penalty)

192. Christian Benteke

193. Andy Carroll

194. Brighton

195. Arsenal

196. Everton

197. Huddersfield Town

198. Wycombe Wanderers

199. Ian Callaghan

200. Alun Evans

## QUIZ 21 · RAFA BENITEZ

201. Burnley

202. Steven Gerrard

203. Fernando Torres

204. Total Network Solutions (TNS)

205. Ryan Babel

206. Benfica

207. Sami Hyypia

208. Chelsea

209. Maccabi Tel Aviv

210. Robbie Fowler

## QUIZ 22 · THE RAFA YEARS

211. Yossi Benayoun

212. Scott Carson

213. Antonio Nunez

214. Tim Cahill

215. Gylfi Sigurdsson

216. Lee Bowyer

217. AK Graz

218. Havant and Waterlooville

219. Hernan Crespo

220. Fabio Cannavaro

## QUIZ 23 · EMRE CAN

221. Bayer Leverkusen

222. Bayern Munich

223. Europa League

224. Watford

225. Real Madrid

226. Arsenal

227. Hoffenheim

228. Maribor

229. Aston Villa

230. Lazar Markovic

## QUIZ 24 · THE GERMAN CONNECTION

231. Manchester City

232. Markus Babbel

233. Fulham

234. Hampden Park

235. Christian Ziege

236. Mainz 05

237. Andriy Voronin

238. Toss of a coin

239. Alun Evans

240. Mats Hummels

## QUIZ 25 · JAMIE CARRAGHER

241. Aston Villa

242. Manchester United

243. Portugal

244. Three
245. Roy Evans
246. Blackburn Rovers
247. Markus Babbel
248. Queens Park Rangers
249. Ian Callaghan
250. Arsenal

## QUIZ 26 · 2005 CHAMPIONS LEAGUE

251. John Arne Riise
252. Paolo Maldini
253. Steven Gerrard
254. Xabi Alonso
255. Michael Owen
256. Andrea Pirlo
257. Djimi Traore
258. Lubos Michel
259. Vladimir Smicer
260. Anthony Le Tallec

## QUIZ 27 · PHILIPPE COUTINHO

261. Inter Milan
262. Bolton Wanderers
263. Espanyol
264. Daniel Sturridge
265. Stoke City
266. Willy Caballero
267. Petr Cech
268. Spartak Moscow
269. Leicester City

270. Manchester United

## QUIZ 28 · TRANSFER MARKET

271. Daniel Sturridge
272. Roma
273. Jamie Redknapp
274. Danny Ings
275. Phil Neal
276. Tottenham Hotspur
277. Mark Kennedy
278. Paris Saint Germain
279. Bjorn Tore Kvarme
280. Newcastle United

## QUIZ 29 · PETER CROUCH

281. Arsenal
282. FB Kaunas
283. Wigan
284. Stephane Henchoz
285. Besiktas
286. Javier Mascherano
287. Burnley
288. Stoke City
289. St. Andrews (Birmingham)
290. John Obi Mikel

## QUIZ 30 · ARSENAL

291. Robbie Fowler
292. Petr Cech
293. Villa Park

294. Sander Westerveld
295. Alan Smith
296. Bernd Leno
297. Patrik Berger
298. Ryan Babel
299. George Graham
300. Jason McAteer

## QUIZ 31 · KENNY DALGLISH

301. West Ham
302. Andy Carroll
303. Derby County
304. Steve McMahon
305. Tottenham Hotspur
306. Brighton
307. Kevin Moran
308. John Barnes
309. Middlesbrough
310. John Aldridge

## QUIZ 32 · CUP COMPETITIONS

311. Ray Clemence
312. Ian Rush
313. Northampton Town
314. Diego Forlan
315. Eric Cantona
316. Olympiakos
317. Mark Seagraves
318. Watford
319. Bobby Mimms
320. Young Boys

## QUIZ 33 · FABINHO

321. Huddersfield Town
322. Eden Hazard
323. Monaco
324. Real Madrid
325. Virgil van Dijk
326. Number 3
327. Gini Wijnaldum
328. Paris Saint-Germain
329. Manchester City
    (with Monaco)
330. Barcelona

## QUIZ 34 · THE SOUTH AMERICAN CONNECTION

331. Alexander Doni
332. Chile
333. Maxi Rodriguez
334. Mauricio Pellegrino
335. Japan
336. Zico
337. Sebastian Coates
338. Nolberto Solano
339. Lucas Leiva
340. Spartak Moscow

## QUIZ 35 · ROBERTO FIRMINO

341. Tottenham Hotspur
342. 2015
343. Hoffenheim

344. Argentina
345. Crystal Palace
346. Porto
347. Manchester City
348. Arsenal
349. Ryan Babel
350. Sevilla

## QUIZ 36 · GOALSCORERS

351. Galatasaray
352. Yossi Benayoun
353. Steven Gerrard (16)
354. West Brom
355. Roberto Firmino
356. Mark Walters
357. Ryan Babel
358. John Toshack
359. Manchester United
360. Mark Viduka

## QUIZ 37 · STEVEN GERRARD

361. Old Trafford
362. Napoli
363. Shaka Hislop
364. Gerard Houllier
365. Munich
366. David James
367. Gary Naysmith
368. Lost 6-1 (Stoke City)
369. Luton Town
370. Vegard Heggem

## QUIZ 38 · ON THE SPOT

371. Paris Saint Gerrmain
372. Gary McAllister
373. Jan Molby
374. Florent Sinama-Pongolle
375. Dave Beasant
376. Queens Park Rangers
377. Sadio Mane
378. Steve McMahon
379. Terry McDermott
380. Billy Liddell

## QUIZ 39 · JOE GOMEZ

381. Gareth Southgate
382. Twelve
383. Burnley
384. Sevilla
385. Charlton Athletic
386. Phil Jones
387. Sadio Mane
388. Philippe Coutinho
389. Bordeaux
390. Left back

## QUIZ 40 · LONDON CONNECTION

391. Jonjo Shelvey
392. Yossi Benayoun
393. Crystal Palace
394. Adrian
395. Jimmy Carter

396. Queens Park Rangers
397. Danny Murphy
398. Teddy Sheringham
399. Sergio Rico
400. Leyton Orient

## QUIZ 41 · DIETMAR HAMANN

401. Newcastle United
402. Liverpool
403. Sheffield Wednesday
404. Steve Finnan
405. Bayer Leverkusen
406. West Ham United
     (2006 FA Cup final)
407. Brazil
408. 16
409. Manchester City
410. Christian Ziege and
     Markus Babbel

## QUIZ 42 · LIVERPOOL AND NEWCASTLE UNITED

411. Alec Lindsay
412. Graeme Souness
413. Faustino Asprilla
414. Andy Carroll
415. Andy Cole
416. Michael Owen
417. Craig Bellamy
418. Jonjo Shelvey
419. Bruno Cheyrou

420. Phil Neal

## QUIZ 43 · GERARD HOULLIER

421. Millennium Stadium, Cardiff
422. Tottenham Hotspur
423. Kiev
424. Basel
425. Gary McAllister
426. Old Trafford
427. Charlton Athletic
428. Robbie Fowler
429. Jean Michel Ferri
430. Southampton

## QUIZ 44 · ALL THINGS FRENCH

431. Nicolas Anelka
432. Marseille
433. Oyvind Leonhardsen
434. Bernard Diomede
435. St Etienne
436. Fabinho
437. Joe Allen
438. Mamadou Sakho
439. Djibril Cisse
440. Kylian Mbappe

## QUIZ 45 · SAMI HYYPIA

441. Ron Yeats
442. MyPa 47
443. Stephane Henchoz
444. Juventus

445. Manchester United
446. Tottenham Hotspur
447. Bayer Leverkusen
448. Fabien Barthez
449. Brighton
450. Joao Carlos Teixeira

## QUIZ 46 · THE NORDIC COUNTRIES

451. Jari Litmanen
452. Eidur Gudjohnsen
453. Bjorn Tore Kvarme
454. Jan Molby
455. Glenn Hysen
456. Oyvind Leonhardsen
457. Christian Poulsen
458. BK Odense
459. Torben Piechnik
460. Stig Inge Bjornebye

## QUIZ 47 · KEVIN KEEGAN

461. Terry McDermott
462. Borussia Moenchengladbach
463. FC Bruges
464. Tommy Smith
465. St.Etienne
466. Doncaster Rovers
467. John Toshack
468. 1974
469. Leicester City
470. Southampton

## QUIZ 48 · FORMER PLAYERS

471. David Burrows
472. David Fairclough
473. Kevin Keegan
474. Stewart Downing
475. Matt Busby
476. Coventry City
477. Mauricio Pellegrino
478. Lazio
479. Burton Albion
480. Mark Walters

## QUIZ 49 · NABY KEITA

481. Huddersfield Town
482. Algeria
483. RB Salzburg
484. Guinea
485. Barcelona
486. Southampton
487. Porto
488. Chester
489. RB Leipzig
490. Peter Gulacsi

## QUIZ 50 · AFRICANS

491. Craig Johnston
492. Charles Itandje
493. Rigobert Song
494. Titi Camara
495. The Toure brothers

496. Momo Sissoko
497. Carl Medjani
498. Morocco
499. Salif Diao
500. Arthur Riley

## QUIZ 51 · JURGEN KLOPP

501. Mainz
502. Chelsea
503. Newcastle United
504. Nuri Sahin
505. Marko Grujic
506. Jordan Ibe and
     Dominic Solanke
507. Tottenham Hotspur
508. Emre Can
509. Daniel Sturridge
510. Chelsea - in the League Cup

## QUIZ 52 · MANAGERS

511. Kenny Dalglish
512. Norwich City
513. Roy Hodgson
514. Arsenal
515. Graeme Souness
516. Roma
517. Manchester United
518. Vegard Heggem
519. George Kay
520. Hibernian

## QUIZ 53 · DIRK KUYT

521. Everton
522. Manchester City
523. Lucas Leiva
524. Feyenoord
525. Chris Kirkland
526. Standard Liege
527. Fenerbahce
528. Andy Carroll
529. Luis Garcia
530. Manchester United

## QUIZ 54 · PENALTIES

531. Mo Salah
     (Champions League final)
532. Riyad Mahrez
533. Harry Kane
534. Jan Molby
535. Theo Walcott
536. Mamadou Sakho
537. Fraser Forster
538. Tottenham Hotspur
539. Billy Liddell
540. Willie Stevenson

## QUIZ 55 · ADAM LALLANA

541. Norwich City
542. Steven Caulker
543. Gareth Bale
544. Rickie Lambert

545. Bournemouth
546. Mo Salah
547. Middlesbrough
548. Slovakia
549. Villarreal
550. Crystal Palace

## QUIZ 56 · LATE WINNERS

551. Ronny Rosenthal
552. Sami Hyypia
553. Manchester City
554. Jamie Redknapp
555. Stan Collymore
556. Paul Gerrard
557. Chelsea
558. Milan Baros (v Crystal Palace)
559. Neil Mellor
560. Christian Benteke

## QUIZ 57 · DEJAN LOVREN

561. France
562. Borussia Dortmund
563. Liverpool
564. Swansea City
565. Southampton
566. Besiktas
567. Manchester City
568. 4-0
569. Luka Modric
570. Kolo Toure

## QUIZ 58 · WORLD CUP

571. Mark Wright
572. Dirk Kuyt
573. Michael Owen
574. Kenny Dalglish
575. Jordan Henderson
576. Senegal
577. Peter Beardsley
578. Karl Heinz Riedle
579. Thomas Meunier
580. Simon Mignolet

## QUIZ 59 · JOEL MATIP

581. Southampton
582. Cameroon
583. Germany
584. Tottenham Hotspur, 2019 Champions League final
585. Schalke 04
586. Crystal Palace
587. One per season
588. West Brom
589. Napoli
590. Brazil

## QUIZ 60 · DEFENDERS

591. Daniel Agger
592. Jose Enrique
593. Steve Staunton
594. Sami Hyypia

595. Jamie Carragher
596. John Scales
597. Stephen Wright
598. Steve Nicol
599. Rob Jones
600. Phil Neal

## QUIZ 61 · SIMON MIGNOLET

601. Jonathan Walters
602. Club Bruges
603. Luis Suarez
604. Brad Jones
605. Stoke City (6-1)
606. Danny Ward
607. Wayne Rooney
608. West Ham United
609. Wolves
610. Peter Crouch

## QUIZ 62 · PREMIER LEAGUE

611. David James
612. Tony Warner
613. Ryan Babel (60)
614. Sheffield Wednesday
615. Ryan Giggs
616. Luis Suarez
617. Coventry City
618. Ipswich Town
619. Jan Molby
620. David Unsworth

## QUIZ 63 · ALBERTO MORENO

621. Sevilla
622. Javier Manquillo
623. Brendan Rodgers
624. Joe Gomez
625. Unai Emery
626. Ivan Rakitic
627. Spartak Moscow
628. Tottenham Hotspur
629. Wolves (FA Cup)
630. Stoke City

## QUIZ 64 · SPANISH CONNECTION

631. Villarreal
632. Fernando Morientes
633. Steve McManaman
634. Iago Aspas
635. Luton Town
636. Albert Riera
637. CSKA Moscow
638. Mikel San Jose
639. Athletic Bilbao
640. John Toshack

## QUIZ 65 · MICHAEL OWEN

641. Alan Shearer
642. Germany
643. Selhurst Park
644. Celtic
645. Newcastle United

646. Roma
647. Stoke City
648. Patrik Berger
649. Steve Heighway
650. Antonio Nunez

## QUIZ 66 · ENGLAND INTERNATIONALS

651. James Milner
652. Emile Heskey
653. Italy
654. Southampton
655. John Barnes
656. Roger Hunt
657. Peter Crouch
658. Steve McManaman
659. Ray Kennedy
660. Phil Neal

## QUIZ 67 · ALEX OXLADE-CHAMBERLAIN

661. Liverpool
662. £35 million
663. Manchester City
664. Maribor
665. Lukasz Fabianski
666. Huddersfield Town
667. Roy Hodgson
668. Brazil
669. Brad Jones
670. Manchester City

## QUIZ 68 · FAMILY TIES

671. Stoke City
672. Mark Hateley (son of Tony)
673. Saunders
674. Rob Jones
675. Alex Watson (brother Dave)
676. Ray Clemence (Stephen Clemence)
677. Nigel Clough (son of Brian)
678. Paul Ince (Tom Ince)
679. Brian and Jimmy Greenhoff
680. Peter Schmeichel (Kasper)

## QUIZ 69 · JAMIE REDKNAPP

681. Bournemouth
682. Kenny Dalglish
683. Auxerre
684. Terry Venables
685. Rene Higuita
686. Southampton
687. Paul Ince
688. Charlton Athletic
689. Birmingham City
690. League Cup

## QUIZ 70 · PUNDITS

691. John Aldridge
692. John Barnes
693. Jim Beglin
694. Stan Collymore

695. Steve McManaman

696. Michael Robinson

697. Nigel Spackman

698. Graeme Souness

699. Danny Murphy

700. Michael Owen

## QUIZ 71 · PEPE REINA

701. Newcastle United

702. Liverpool in UEFA Cup semi-final 2001

703. Villarreal

704. Three

705. Paul Konchesky

706. Iker Casillas

707. Brad Jones

708. Rafa Benitez

709. Atletico Madrid

710. Arsenal

## QUIZ 72 · SENDINGS OFF

711. Barnsley

712. Igor Biscan

713. El Hadji-Diouf

714. Phil Neville and Mikel Arteta

715. Tottenham Hotspur

716. Ian St John

717. Luis Garcia

718. Steve McManaman

719. Chelsea

720. Inter Milan

## QUIZ 73 · ANDREW ROBERTSON

721. Brighton

722. Dominic Solanke

723. Hull City

724. Dundee United

725. Huddersfield Town

726. Luis Suarez

727. Gordon Strachan

728. England

729. Hampden Park

730. Crystal Palace

## QUIZ 74 · THE SCOTTISH CONNECTION

731. Gary McAllister

732. Charlie Adam

733. Steve Nicol

734. Graeme Souness

735. Don Hutchison

736. Ron Yeats

737. Peter Cormack

738. David Speedie

739. Tommy Lawrence

740. Gary Gillespie

## QUIZ 75 · IAN RUSH

741. Chester

742. Everton

743. 1993

744. Blackburn Rovers

745. John Barnes

746. Roger Hunt

747. Roy Evans

748. Michael Thomas

749. Arsenal

750. Stan Collymore

## QUIZ 76 · THE WELSH CONNECTION

751. Joe Allen

752. Birmingham City

753. Craig Bellamy

754. Dean Saunders

755. Chris Coleman

756. Harry Wilson

757. Paul Jones

758. Joey Jones

759. Steven Gerrard
(Anthony Gerrard)

760. John Toshack

## QUIZ 77 · MOHAMED SALAH

761. Watford

762. James Milner

763. Everton

764. Fernando Torres

765. Liverpool (with Chelsea)

766. Stoke City

767. 32

768. Dean Court (or Vitality Stadium), Bournemouth

769. Dean Saunders

770. Basel

## QUIZ 78 · HAT-TRICKS

771. Robbie Fowler

772. Michael Owen

773. Gordon Hodgson

774. Mark Walters

775. Neville Southall

776. Manchester City

777. Stan Collymore

778. Matt Le Tissier

779. Steve Staunton

780. Julio Baptista

## QUIZ 79 · XHERDAN SHAQIRI

781. Cardiff City

782. Manchester United

783. Philipp Degen

784. Andrew Robertson

785. Southampton

786. Red Star Belgrade

787. Wesley Hoedt

788. Bayern Munich

789. Basel

790. Honduras

## QUIZ 80 · INTERNATIONALS

791. Danny Ings, Paul Ince

792. Ragnar Klavan

793. Germany

794. Phil Neal

795. Steve McManaman

796. Alan Hansen

797. John Arne Riise

798. Jari Litmanen

799. Igor Biscan

800. Billy Liddell

## QUIZ 81 · MARTIN SKRTEL

801. Tottenham Hotspur

802. Slovakia

803. Havant and Waterlooville

804. Carlos Tevez

805. Fenerbahce

806. Manchester City

807. Cardiff City (League Cup final)

808. Arsenal

809. Zenit St. Petersburg

810. Diego Costa

## QUIZ 82 · THE TOTTENHAM CONNECTION

811. Harry Kane

812. Jamie Carragher

813. Teddy Sheringham

814. Robbie Keane

815. Brad Friedel

816. James Milner

817. Jon Flanagan

818. Jimmy Greaves

819. Steve Heighway

820. Phil Boersma

## QUIZ 83 · VLADIMIR SMICER

821. Harry Kewell

822. Lens

823. Patrik Berger

824. Bordeaux

825. Manchester City

826. Carlo Cudicini

827. Britannia Stadium (Stoke)

828. Crystal Palace

829. Arsenal

830. Russia

## QUIZ 84 · SUBSTITUTES

831. Daniel Sturridge

832. Steven Gerrard

833. Florent Sinama-Pongolle

834. Adam Lallana

835. John Aldridge

836. Jamie Redknapp

837. Howard Gayle

838. Steve Staunton

839. Xherdan Shaqiri

840. Geoff Strong

## QUIZ 85 · DANIEL STURRIDGE

841. Manchester United

842. West Ham United

843. Manchester City

844. Jonjo Shelvey

845. Brad Guzan

846. Manchester United

847. Adrian

848. Chelsea

849. Trabzonspor

850. Ray Kennedy

## QUIZ 86 · MANCHESTER CITY

851. Daniel Sturridge

852. James Milner

853. Alex Oxlade-Chamberlain

854. Riyad Mahrez

855. George Weah

856. Jan Molby

857. Ian Rush

858. Robbie Fowler

859. 10 - Liverpool won 6-0 & 4-0

860. Kevin Bond (son of John)

## QUIZ 87 · LUIS SUAREZ

861. Ajax

862. Stoke City

863. Ghana

864. Sylvain Distin

865. Oldham Athletic

866. Newcastle United

867. Raheem Sterling

868. Crystal Palace

869. Daniel Sturridge

870. Joe Hart

## QUIZ 88 · OVERSEAS INTERNATIONALS

871. Thierry Henry (8)

872. Branislav Ivanovic

873. Benfica

874. Raul Meireles

875. Jaap Stam

876. Jean Tigana

877. Iker Casillas

878. Rivaldo

879. Fabrizio Ravanelli

880. Alaves (2001 UEFA Cup final - the first Golden Goal in a final)

## QUIZ 89 · THE 1960s

881. Billy Liddell

882. Arsenal

883. Gary Sprake (Leeds United)

884. Coventry City

885. Ian Callaghan

886. Luton Town

887. Bobby Graham

888. Emlyn Hughes

889. Gordon Banks

890. Malmo

## QUIZ 90 · THE 1970s

891. John Toshack
892. Hull City
893. Filbert Street
894. Graeme Souness
895. Ipswich Town
896. Phil Boersma
897. Peter McDonnell
898. Four
899. Tommy Wright
900. Barcelona

## QUIZ 91 · PHIL THOMPSON

901. West Ham
902. Barcelona
903. Paris
904. Larry Lloyd
905. Malcolm Macdonald
906. Italy
907. John O'Hare
908. Sheffield United
909. Hamburg (Super Cup)
910. John Toshack

## QUIZ 92 · LIVERPOOL CUP CAMPAIGNS

911. Lionel Messi
912. John Arne Riise
913. Arsenal
914. Anthony Martial

915. Benfica
916. Crystal Palace
917. Steve Nicol
918. Dundalk
919. Tottenham Hotspur
920. Wycombe Wanderers

## QUIZ 93 · KOLO TOURE

921. Celtic
922. Ivory Coast
923. Sevilla
    (Europa League final)
924. Christian Benteke
925. Sion
926. Fulham
927. Victor Anichebe
928. Aston Villa
929. Millennium Stadium
    (Community Shield)
930. Number 4

## QUIZ 94 · THE OLD FIRM CONNECTION

931. Craig Bellamy
932. Graeme Souness
933. John Barnes
934. Alan Thompson
935. Henrik Larsson
936. Sotirios Kyrgiakos
937. Virgil van Dijk

938. Steve McManaman

939. Mark Walters

940. Willie Stevenson

## QUIZ 95 · VIRGIL VAN DIJK

941. Alex Oxlade-Chamberlain

942. Molineux

943. Celtic

944. Manchester City

945. Watford

946. Red Star Belgrade

947. Teemu Pukki

948. Sadio Mane

949. Ronald Koeman

950. Six

## QUIZ 96 · AWARDS

951. Mo Salah

952. Luis Suarez

953. Steven Gerrard

954. Kenny Dalglish

955. Ian Callaghan

956. Steve Nicol

957. Robbie Fowler

958. John Wark

959. Paul Walsh

960. Terry McDermott

## QUIZ 97 · RONNIE WHELAN

961. Tottenham Hotspur

962. Ray Kennedy

963. Roy Evans

964. Jackie Charlton

965. Stoke City

966. Manchester United

967. Portsmouth

968. USSR

969. Southend United

970. Home Farm

## QUIZ 98 · THE IRISH CONNECTION

971. Ronnie Whelan

972. Jason McAteer

973. Ray Houghton

974. Steve Finnan

975. Mark Lawrenson

976. Michael Robinson

977. Tranmere Rovers

978. Mark Kennedy

979. Steve Staunton

980. Holland

## QUIZ 99 · GEORGINIO WIJNALDUM

981. Newcastle United

982. Portugal

983. Wembley (v Tottenham)

984. Alisson (with Roma)

985. Cardiff City

986. Ryan Babel

987. James Milner

988. Middlesbrough

989. Manchester City

990. Chelsea

## QUIZ 100 · MIDFIELDERS

991. Joe Cole

992. Nuri Sahin

993. Danny Murphy

994. Paul Ince

995. Olivier Dacourt

996. Dietmar Hamann

997. Gary McAllister

998. Jimmy Case

999. Terry McDermott

1000. Vladimir Smicer